FROGGY PLAYS SOCCER

FROGGY PLAYS SOCCER

by JONATHAN LONDON
illustrated by FRANK REMKIEWICZ

SCHOLASTIC INC.
New York   Toronto   London   Auckland   Sydney
Mexico City   New Delhi   Hong Kong

For the Dream Team: Sean, Max, Matthew, Travis, B.J., Joseph, Jeff, Rickey, Juan, Goose, Marcos, Dave, Kyler, Bobby, and their coach, Jacqueline Keywood Hammerman
       —J. L.

For José, Kyle, and Anna, champions all.
       —F. R.

ISBN 0-439-08641-8

Text copyright © 1999 by Jonathan London. Illustrations copyright © 1999 by Frank Remkiewicz.
All rights reserved. Published by Scholastic Inc., 555 Broadway, New York, NY 10012,
by arrangement with Viking Children's Books, a division of Penguin Putnam Inc.
SCHOLASTIC and associated logos are trademarks and/or registered trademarks of Scholastic Inc.

36 35 34 33 32   7 8 9/0

Printed in the U.S.A.   08

First Scholastic printing, March 2000
Set in Kabel

Froggy couldn't sleep.
He looked out the window.
The full moon was rising.
It looked like a soccer ball.
"Tomorrow's the big game!"
he said out loud.
"If we beat the Wild Things
we win the City Cup!"

In the morning,
Froggy was bursting to go.
He pulled on his underwear—*zap!*

Tugged on his
soccer shorts—*zeep!*
Snapped on his
shin guards—*znap!*

Wiggled on his
soccer shirt—*zlim!*
Pulled on his
soccer socks—*zoop!*

And put on his
cleats—*zup! zup!*

FRROOGGYY!

called his father. Froggy's father was the assistant coach.

"Wha-a-a-a-t?"

"Let's go! We'll be late for the game!"

Froggy flopped outside—*flop flop flop.*

"Remember," said Froggy's dad,
"only the goalie can catch the ball—
and you're not the goalie!

"Now repeat after me:
Head it!
Boot it!
Knee it!
Shoot it!
BUT DON'T USE YOUR HANDS!"

And Froggy sang:
"Head it!

Boot it!

Knee it! Shoot it!
BUT DON'T USE YOUR HANDS! . . ."
all the way to the soccer field.

At the soccer field,
the coach, Max's mother, said,

"We're a *team*.
We're the Dream Team!"
"*Hurray!*" screamed
the Dream Team.

Soon, the game was on!
Froggy was
doing cartwheels.

Froggy was
picking daisies.

Froggy was picking his nose.

The ball bounced
off his chest.
He gave a mighty kick—

and missed the ball.

But Max trapped it and passed it to B.J.
who slammed it right into the net—*goal!*

It was one to zero—Dream Team!

Again, the two teams faced off. The whistle blew.
The Dream Team charged down the field toward the Wild Things.
Froggy was tying his shoe.

Froggy's dad was yelling, "Defense! Defense!"
The ball hit Froggy in the head—*bonk!*—
and knocked him down.
He was great at defense.

At halftime,
the Dream Team held the lead.
"Now remember . . . "
said Froggy's dad,
and they all chanted together:
"Head it!
Boot it!
Knee it!
Shoot it!
BUT DON'T USE YOUR HANDS!"

The whistle blew
and the second half started.
A fly circled by.

FRROOGGYY !

called the coach.

"Wha-a-a-a-a-t?"
"Keep your eye on the—"
Thwap! The ball smacked
him in the eye.

Froggy was mad now.
The Wild Things were stampeding.
And Matthew, the Dream Team's goalkeeper,
was chasing the ball.
Now the goal was unguarded.
This was Froggy's chance!
He leapfrogged over Travis.
He leapfrogged over Matthew.

He leapfrogged over the Wild Things' forward
who was firing the ball . . .

and what a save!
Froggy caught it right before the net.
But, *uh-oh*—he'd used his *hands*!

"Oops!" cried Froggy,
looking more red in the face than green.
He looked so silly, the Dream Team laughed.
But not for long.

The penalty for using his hands was
a free kick at the goal for the Wild Things.
The Wild Things' star forward kicked . . .
and scored. Now it was a tied game!

But it wasn't over yet.
And when there was one minute left
the crowd went crazy.
The clock was ticking.
The ball was coming right toward Froggy.

FRROOGGYY!

yelled his dad.
"Wha-a-a-a-t?"
But Froggy knew what to do.

He jammed his hands
in his armpits.

He stuffed them
in his pockets.

He stuck them in his mouth.

Then he power-kicked the ball
so far down the field
that it bounced over the goalie's head . . .

smack into the goal.
YES!

The Dream Team had won the City Cup!
They shouted and danced.
And Froggy sang:
"Head it!
Boot it!
Knee it!
Shoot it!
BUT DON'T USE YOUR HANDS!—

"except to slap high fives!"—*slap   slap   slap!*

Don't
Forget to
Share

The Crucial Last Step in
the Writing Workshop

Leah Mermelstein

Foreword by
Carl Anderson

HEINEMANN
Portsmouth, NH

Heinemann
A division of Reed Elsevier Inc.
361 Hanover Street
Portsmouth, NH 03801–3912
www.heinemann.com

Offices and agents throughout the world

Library of Congress Cataloging-in-Publication Data
Mermelstein, Leah.
  Don't forget to share : the crucial last step in the writing workshop
/ Leah Mermelstein.
       p. cm.
  Includes bibliographical references and index.
  ISBN-13: 978-0-325-00951-3 (pbk. : alk. paper)
  ISBN-10: 0-325-00951-1
  1. English language—Composition and exercises—Study and teaching.
2. Forums (Discussion and debate). 3. Authorship—Collaboration.
4. Group work in education. I. Title.
  LB1576.M455   2007
  808'.042071—dc22   2006034977

Editor: Harvey Daniels
Production: Patricia Adams
Typesetter: SPi Publisher Services
Cover design: Gina Poirier Design
Manufacturing: Louise Richardson

Printed in the United States of America on acid-free paper
11   10   09   08   07   RRD   1   2   3   4   5

To Erica Denman

Contents

Appendices

Foreword

In today's educational climate—one dominated by the pressures of high-stakes testing—it can seem risky to have an ambitious vision for the writing workshop. Some of us might respond to talk of such a vision by saying, *What you're saying sounds great, but with all that I have to do in my classroom, there just isn't the* time *to do what you're talking about.*

Leah Mermelstein has an ambitious vision for the writing workshop, which she details in her book *Don't Forget to Share: The Crucial Last Step in the Writing Workshop*. She expects that during every writing workshop, students will talk together as a class about their writing in sophisticated ways that will help them learn from each other about how to grow as writers. In the book, Leah shows us how we can do this, but *not* by suggesting another structure that we'll have to shoehorn into our already jam-packed writing workshop time. Instead, Leah helps us reimagine how an already existing part of our writing workshop, the share session, can be the time when these conversations can take place.

Traditionally, the share session has been a time when one student would sit on the author's chair and read his piece to the class. Afterward, the student would field a few questions about the content of his piece. For several reasons, many teachers have abandoned this kind of share session, one being that they felt the questions students asked were superficial ones and didn't support meaningful revisions. Instead, many teachers today use share session time as a kind of show-and-tell. One or two students talk about something interesting they did that period in their current piece of writing—often in response to that day's minilesson—as the rest of the students listen and (hopefully) hear about something they could try in their writing.

In *Don't Forget to Share*, Leah revises the conventional thinking about shares. While in this book, you'll see examples of shares in which students still sit *on* the author's chair and read their pieces, and in which students still talk to the class about what they did as writers during that period, Leah helps us imagine how these experiences can lead to rich whole-class conversations that can impact *every* student in the class as a writer.

Moreover, Leah helps us see that there can be different kinds of conversations in share sessions. In some shares, for example, the students will discuss the *content* of one or two students' pieces, and through the discussion, they will discover ways that all of them can revise their pieces. In other shares, students will talk about the *craft* techniques that several of their classmates have used in their writing and, as a result of this talk, be able to imagine how to craft their own writing in these new ways. And on other days, the students will discuss their *writing processes* and teach each other about their ways of navigating the different steps in the writing process. In these kinds of shares, and the others that Leah talks about in the book, students learn about strategies and techniques they'll need to become strong writers.

I admire how clear and practical Leah is throughout the book. Knowing Leah as I do—we were colleagues at the Teachers College Reading and Writing Project at Columbia University for several years—this doesn't surprise me. Leah was known throughout the project community for the clarity of her thinking and for ideas that really work in classrooms. Throughout the book are transcripts of shares conducted by Leah or one of the teachers with whom she works. There are also numerous tips for you to follow to have similar shares in your writing workshop. I'm certain that you'll feel excited to try out the different kinds of share sessions that Leah discusses right away and that Leah will give you the know-how and confidence you'll need to be successful.

I can't imagine that after you read *Don't Forget to Share* you'll say that you don't have the time to do the ambitious teaching that Leah discusses in this book. You already have the time built in to your writing workshop. As Leah helps us see, it's how we choose to use the time we have that makes the biggest difference in our students' growth as writers. In these challenging times, I find Leah's book to be not only practical but inspirational, too.

—*Carl Anderson*

Acknowledgments

It certainly is fitting that a book on sharing has been influenced by so many people who have graciously shared their thinking and experiences with me. I begin by thanking Wendy Appelgate, Adrienne Genaro, Dustie Zocher, Sally Juzeler, Shellie Hatch, Pauline Shenyer, Marsha Childrers, Desiree Mains, Camille Klingele, Beth Buchholz, and Amanda Wilson. This dynamic group of teachers and administrators agreed to join me in studying the share session, and many of the ideas in this book were born during our long and often lively leadership meetings. I thank them for trying the ideas in their classrooms and for sharing what did and did not work. A special thank-you to Pauline Shenyer's daughter, Leah, who crafted her thoughts about sharing into a gorgeous poem that she so graciously let me use in this book. I thank Daniel Scott O'Neill for taking the cover photograph.

Helen Yu from PS 1 and Ellen McCrum from PS 234 were my local leadership team. This book is far more practical and teacher friendly because of them, and I thank them for their honesty about what they thought teachers needed in order to conduct shares effectively in their classrooms. I thank Amy Hom and Sandy Bridges, the principals of PS 1 and PS 234, for welcoming me into their schools and for letting me watch many wonderful share sessions in action.

I also thank my mentor, Lucy Calkins. I will forever be grateful for all the ways she has supported me professionally. I especially thank her for asking me to join her in coauthoring *Launching the Writing Workshop*. Through that collaboration I learned how to design a book that includes rich theory alongside practical teaching ideas.

I also want to thank Carl Anderson for graciously writing my foreword. Carl has always been a mentor to me and I thank him for always sharing both his thinking and his advice with me.

There were many people who took time out of their busy lives to read my manuscript and offer me thoughtful critique. Erica Denman, Shawn Brandon, Helen Yu, and Ellen McCrum all read the manuscript at critical junctures, and their wise feedback always reenergized me to keep searching for the clearest ways to explain complicated ideas. I also thank Norman Stiles for reminding me that the best way to revise is to write straight from the heart.

I thank Isoke Nia, Linda Chen, Kathy Collins, Randy Bomer, Katherine Bomer, Cheryl Tyler, Katie Wood Ray, Gaby Layden, Ellen Dillon, Carl Anderson, Lisa Burman, Donna Santman, Grace Chough, Annemarie Powers, and Janet Angelillo for being my reading and writing "companions in thought." Thank you for always challenging me to rethink and revise my beliefs about best ways to teach both reading and writing.

Most of my days are spent working side by side with principals, staff developers, teachers, and students. This book is graced with their brilliant work. I thank everyone from the Prosser Elementary Schools, Schenendehowa Elementary Schools, Guilderland Elementary Schools, Norwalk Elementary Schools, Greenwich Elementary Schools, Springs Elementary School in East Hampton, PS 59, the Learning Community Charter School, Roxbury Elementary School, and Lake George Elementary School.

Of course, I also thank the entire team at Heinemann for their support in putting this book together. A special thanks goes to Kate Mongomery for thinking through this book with me in its earliest stages. I admire her brilliance, her sense of adventure, and her attention to detail. Thanks also to my editor, Harvey Daniels. His words of encouragement always brought a sense of playfulness to my writing, and I thank him for always making his insightful suggestions in a kind and fun-loving manner. I thank Alan Huisman for reading my text with such a careful eye. I thank production editor Patty Adams for her time and attention to my book at its final stages.

Finally, I want to thank my parents and first teachers, Terry and Lothar Mermelstein, who continue to teach me important lessons about living and learning.

Overview

I have spent the last ten years, first as a teacher, then as a staff developer, and now as a guest speaker, studying alongside Lucy Calkins and her cadre of brilliant staff developers at the Teachers College Reading and Writing Project. You'll see the influence of that collaboration throughout the book, especially in the terminology that I use when describing the teaching of writing. For some of you, especially those of you familiar with the work that comes out of Teachers College, these terms will be familiar. For others, some of the terms might be new or used in a slightly different way.

Throughout the book I refer to the *writing workshop*. A writing workshop is a time in each school day (approximately forty-five minutes to one hour) when you explicitly teach students how to become better writers. A typical writing workshop has a three-part structure: minilesson, work time, and share session. The first part, the minilesson, is usually between ten and fifteen minutes long. It is a time to gather your whole class together to teach the students something new about writing. Nancie Atwell describes the minilesson as a "brief lecture at the start of class about procedures, conventions, craft, genre and topic development" (1998, 15). After the minilesson, there is a work time of about thirty-five minutes during which students work on their own individual writing pieces. During this same time, the teacher confers with students one-on-one or in small groups about their specific strengths and needs. The writing workshop ends with a share session of about ten minutes.

The share session is the focus of this book. As you'll soon discover, many different things can happen during this time, but it should be an opportunity for students to have writerly conversations with one another. These conversations can be in a whole class, in small groups, or in pairs (some people refer to the paired partnership as *pair share* or *buddy work*).

Many writing workshop teachers not only conduct a daily writing workshop but also plan their writing curriculum in advance. They create a monthly curriculum of *units of study*. A unit of study is a road map for what you'll teach over a period of time (usually between two and six weeks) in your writing workshop. Lucy Calkins describes the benefits of using units of study this way: they "allow teachers to plan and organize a sequence of instruction so that over time students successfully tackle new and often increasingly difficult challenges" (2003, 19). Some examples of possible units of study are Launching the Writing Workshop, Narrative Writing, Authors as Mentors, Partnerships, Memoir, Fiction, and Writing About Reading. During a unit of study, students are going through the steps of the writing process. Some of these steps are rehearsal (or brainstorming), drafting, revising, editing, and publishing. The students typically take at least one of their writing pieces through *all* of the steps, and then teachers bring the study to a close by planning a writing celebration. Most K–2 students store this writing in a writing folder, and most upper-grade students begin keeping a writer's notebook, which they use as a springboard for their drafts.

Units of study often begin with something called *immersion*. Immersion is a period of time (two to five days) when students, rather than writing, are being saturated with the genre or topic being studied. The purpose of immersion is for kids to notice how a particular type of text is written. This is often referred to as *craft*. If a class was being immersed in nonfiction, for example, the teacher might begin by reading quality nonfiction literature and then asking her students to do the same. They would notice elements of craft such as headings, diagrams, and descriptive language. After noticing these, kids would be encouraged to try those very same techniques when writing their own nonfiction texts.

During a unit of study, teachers often select and use *touchstone texts*. Touchstone texts are pieces of literature that the students know and love and that can be used throughout a unit of study as another way of teaching craft. If I wanted to show my students how to use vivid description, for example, I might use Julie Brinkloe's *Fireflies* as a touchstone text, showing them the page on which she writes, "It was growing dark. My tree house was a black shape in the tree and I wouldn't go up there now" (1985, 2). I would let my students know that just as Julie Brinkloe uses very particular words to describe what the setting looked like, they can as well. Many teachers decide to have a few touchstone texts for every unit of study, and I've included some of my favorites in Appendix C.

Writing teachers plan their yearly instruction by creating a *curriculum calendar*. Whereas a unit of study details approximately a month of teaching, a curriculum calendar details a year of teaching. Usually, a curriculum calendar is organized by the months of the school year and consists of between eight and fifteen units of study. These studies should be varied; that is, teachers should include some genre units of study (such as nonfiction), some process units of study (such as partnerships), and some craft units of study (such as author studies). Curriculum calendars should also include some longer units of study (four, five, or six weeks) alongside shorter units of study (one, two, or three weeks).

This book focuses primarily on the share session; however, while reading it, you'll discover how shares connect to the aspects of writing instruction I just described. If you are interested in learning more about the writing workshop, please refer to the book list in Appendix A. For more information visit my website at http://leahmermelstein.com.

Welcome to Share Sessions: The Special Power of Conversation

Writers need to talk about their writing, and the thing that seems to make or break many writing workshops is the presence (or absence) of productive talk.

—Katie Wood Ray, *Wondrous Words*

Have you ever had a conversation and walked away thinking, *That was exactly what I needed to hear*? I had one of those wonderful kinds of talks recently with my editor, Harvey Daniels. I had been suffering from writer's block: day in and day out I sat staring at my computer, at an utter loss for words. After a week of this torture, it was clear that more writing time was not the answer. What I really needed was a good writing conversation. So I scheduled a phone meeting with Harvey, beforehand identifying a few things I wanted to talk about. I'm sure he did the same. However, the power of our conversation wasn't in what we had planned but in what happened when we expressed our thinking to each other. I left our discussion reenergized: I couldn't wait to articulate in writing all that we had talked about.

Just as I do my best writing when I'm surrounded by conversation, my students do too. A share session is the perfect time for kids to have writerly conversations with one another as a class, in small groups, and in pairs. But for these discussions to go well, they must be carefully orchestrated. This book gives you an inside look at teachers who have turned their share sessions into times when kids speak with, listen to, and learn from one another.

Here's a poem about sharing, written by Leah Shenyer, a third grader:

Sharing

Loneliness shared makes friends.
Friendships bring care, joy, and laughter.
Laughter heard
Fills the world
With bits and pieces of all of us.
Bad times grow into good times.
Sad times turn out to be fun times.
Imagine!
What a world it would be!
Who will YOU share with today?

My favorite phrase is "bits and pieces of all of us." It's a perfect description of what sharing should look like in the world. Whether you're sharing how your day went with your family, or your students are sharing their thoughts about a book, these conversations should be bits and pieces of the people who are having them.

Leah's wise words aptly describe the private share sessions I have with my family and friends. We share our good times and our bad times and get through life's trials and tribulations by offering one another our insights and opinions. I only wish I had taken Leah's poem more to heart during the sharing that used to take place in my writing workshops.

In my work as a reading and writing consultant, during which I conduct workshops for teachers as well as work side by side with them in their classrooms, my goal is always to help them conduct a joyful and rigorous writing workshop. I've always spoken at great length about minilessons and conferences as perfect tools for teaching students more about writing. But in the past I've ignored the share session, because quite frankly I didn't understand the value of it. When I did conduct shares I would usually have a few kids read their writing aloud and talk about what they had tried. I spent most of my time reminding the other kids that it was their job to listen. There were very few bits and pieces of any of my students in these earlier shares, and in my heart of hearts I knew the children were not benefiting from them.

After many such unsuccessful share sessions, I started letting the kids write for a longer time or even skipping the share altogether. When it was time to share, the teachers observing my lessons would

Don't Forget to Share: The Crucial Last Step in the Writing Workshop

nod a quiet good-bye and return to their classrooms: they didn't expect anything of substance to take place.

Feeling frustrated with my shares (and knowing I was neglecting this part of the writing workshop), I decided to speak with some teachers about my dilemma. I soon discovered that I was not alone. They were feeling the same dissatisfaction and wished there were a way to make their shares more productive. I began to wonder: Was there a way to make the sharing during writing time feel more like the sharing that people did in their real lives?

Reading what others had said about share sessions, I discovered that although many brilliant people had touched on them, no one had examined them in depth. Don Graves, the grandfather of writing workshop, wrote about the importance of share meetings and offered some concrete suggestions on what to do:

> For about five to eight minutes after each writing period it is helpful to share writing experiences. Material shared can be any number of the following:
>
> 1. What were some of the topics of this morning?
> 2. How did it go? (After some sharing by the children, share some of your struggles and learning.)
> 3. Sharing: Would anybody like to read what he or she has so far? Even just read one line that you like? (1983, 16)

Graves understood that share meetings were the perfect way to honor and respect individual writers, as well as give them an authentic audience, but later he realized that this was not enough. He revised his original vision of the ideal share session, suggesting that teachers pay attention not only to the person sharing but to the listeners as well (1994, 133). Katie Wood Ray (2001, 177) highlighted the importance of kids talking a lot during the share session and taking responsibility for that talk, and Lucy Calkins, in *The Nuts and Bolts of Teaching Writing* (2003, 42), recommended that teachers use the share session as an additional time to teach.

All of what these authorities said is true. Shares should honor kids' accomplishments. Kids should have an authentic audience for their writing. They do need to listen to one another. These meetings should be filled with lots and lots of kid talk. And of course we should be teaching during shares. But I still wondered exactly how to go about doing that. What would it look like to conduct shares in which I gave kids the opportunity to speak and listen to one another and then taught into what they were saying? I decided to explore this question by working with teachers and students in their classrooms. I conducted share session after share session with this single question in mind, and this book is the result.

The Art of Conversation

As I've begun to conduct share sessions as discussions, I've been dazzled by the ways in which these meetings have the capacity to lift energy, build morale, encourage participation, and most of all instruct. The act—and the art—of conversation helps students return to their writing, as I did, with a renewed vigor to fill up the blank page. Why? There are three reasons:

1. In a writing conversation, kids make important instructional decisions.

2. In a writing conversation, kids use their own language to explain complicated ideas.

3. In a writing conversation, kids get to linger over ideas.

Making Their Own Instructional Decisions

Recently, I gathered a class of kindergartners. "Today I noticed that some of you finished early, and you weren't sure what to do next. Let's talk together about some of the things you can do to keep yourself writing the entire time."

Ideas poured in from all corners of the room. "You can add pages." "You can add words." "You can start a new story." Students were teaching one another what I had planned to teach in my minilessons for the entire week! Every student was enthusiastic and participated in the conversation, and I know it was because the children were making their own decisions about how to make their writing workshop better. Since I was also a contributor to the conversation, I could have pointed out ideas that seemed inappropriate, but I find that kids take these writing conversations very seriously and rarely suggest unworkable or goofy ideas.

Don't Forget to Share: The Crucial Last Step in the Writing Workshop

Kids not only get to make decisions about what will be taught but also get to choose which parts of the conversation they'll put to use immediately and which parts they'll tuck away for another day. Teachers often ask how to differentiate instruction in the minilesson. It's a great question. There are certainly little things we can do in a minilesson to address the needs of all our learners, but we can better address their individual needs in a share, where a number of ideas arise naturally, and kids can choose the one that's the best fit for them. Let me show you what I mean.

Just the other day, a teacher told me about her most recent share session. One student shared the index he had created for his nonfiction book—not just the end product but also how he had gone about creating it. After the students asked him some questions, they all went back and reread their own writing, deciding if they wanted to include an index. The next student shared her nonfiction piece about dogs. One of her classmates asked her about the different colors of dogs, and after she answered the question, she decided to revise and include the color of the dogs in her piece. The rest of the kids once again reread their writing, deciding whether they should include color words. Finally, another child shared how he ended his nonfiction piece with a question, and a few students discovered that they wanted to include questions in their own writing. In this instance students chose how the share conversation affected their writing.

When students initiate and make decisions about instruction, they are more likely to follow through. I was pleasantly surprised by how quickly the kindergartners I previously described stopped saying "I'm done" during writing workshop and became more independent problem solvers. Another benefit of students making instructional decisions is that great topics arise that we may not have considered teaching. For example, an index isn't likely to come up in a teacher's minilessons. Another teacher told me recently that during one of her share sessions, the kids started talking about how to add humor to a writing piece. Students grabbed on to one another's ideas and quite artfully began adding humor to their writing. This teacher said she probably never would have thought about teaching humor to her students, but their discussion about it ended up improving the quality of their writing dramatically.

Using Their Own Language to Explain Complicated Ideas

At times, we attempt to teach our students and fail miserably because the words we use just don't make sense to them. If they can come up with their own way of saying things, it's a lot easier for others to grasp the ideas. The share session gives kids that opportunity. Recently, Edward, a third grader, shared how he had discovered that his story really was, as he put it, "two stories crammed into one." He explained that he solved this problem by first separating the one "crammed-together" story into two separate "not crammed-together" stories. I watched the other students listen to his explanation with rapt attention, knowing full well that his teacher had been trying to explain this concept for weeks. After Edward had finished, I asked the students to reread their writing to see if they had two stories crammed into one. For the first time many students were able to see this issue in their writing, and it was Edward's explanation that helped it sink in. There is no way I could have given a lesson on focus that was more pointed than Edward's even if I'd tried.

Lingering over Ideas

In any lively conversation our minds are working like crazy! We're reflecting, evaluating, critiquing, usually all at the same time. It's no different in a share session conversation, and because of this we're inclined to stick with ideas for a longer time, which of course makes it more memorable. More than this, however, our thinking is further slowed down because we are talking with others. Each person not only lingers over her own ideas but is also hearing what others think, which enables her to understand the topic from multiple perspectives.

Ellen McCrum, a fifth-grade teacher, recently conducted a share session in which her kids discussed whether or not the main characters' actions, thoughts, and spoken words in their fictional but realistic stories should match their own personalities. Students talked animatedly about this dilemma, and while a consensus or neat answer was never found, the children had a much richer understanding of how to build the world of a character because they had lingered over one another's ideas.

Don't Forget to Share: The Crucial Last Step in the Writing Workshop

Getting Started

You are now probably wondering, *How often should I conduct share sessions? How do I gather my students? What do I need?* These are all important questions.

If you want your students to become adept at having writerly conversations, you must set aside the last ten or fifteen minutes of each day's writing workshop for a share meeting. Many teachers tell me, "Most days I plan to do a share, but then I see the students working so well. I just don't want to stop them." I understand that feeling, but if you don't conduct regular share sessions, your kids won't get enough practice at having these types of conversations. Let your students know that share sessions will be a vital part of every writing workshop. Then do whatever it takes to conduct one: set a timer, ask a student to remind you, put it in your plan book—anything that will ensure that it happens every day.

You'll also need a place for your students to gather. Because your share sessions are conversations, they'll go best if students face one another in a circle. Many teachers conduct their share sessions on a rug or in an area of the classroom marked off in some other way. Some teachers assign students a place in the circle, while others let students decide that for themselves. Some teachers ask students to bring their chairs over to the area, while others have the kids sit directly on the carpet or the floor. Whatever your approach, join them in the share circle. As you'll soon see, you are an important contributor!

Once you've found a place for your class to convene, you'll want to think about the materials you and your students will need. What students bring will vary each day, so they'll need some direction. The most common materials I ask students to bring are the piece of writing they're currently working on, a pen or a pencil, their writing folder (primary grades) or their writing notebook (middle and upper grades), and/or a piece of literature they've been reading in the classroom (a touchstone text).

You'll also want some standard supplies handy in case you and your students need to use them. Some things I keep within arm's reach are sticky notes, touchstone texts, extra paper, and revision and editing tape. I also keep my recordkeeping system close at hand so I can note my observations as well as ideas for future instruction. (See Appendix D for recordkeeping ideas.)

Types of Share Meetings

So far, I've imagined share sessions as times when students can have lively, instructional conversations with one another. Now, we're ready to dig in and study exactly what these discussions might look like. Figure 1.1 is an overview of the four types of whole-class shares you'll learn about in the following chapters. In some types of shares, nobody's writing is being discussed; in others, only a few students' writing is being talked about. This may surprise you. You're probably used to having more students read their writing aloud in a share session.

In the past, right before the share session, kids would surround me, begging to share. It was difficult to say no, so I would end up with a rather large crowd expecting to read their writing. It was tough to get any real conversation going: just having the kids read used up all the time. Because I want the share to be a place for rich conversation, I now choose only a few kids to share, and we talk longer about each piece of writing. (Over time I do make sure that everyone gets a chance.)

Because fewer kids are sharing, it's important that you think carefully about other ways that students can participate. I've therefore included several suggested techniques in Figure 1.1 that you can use to ensure that all students join in the conversation. You'll see these techniques in action throughout the book. In addition, Chapter 7 discusses how you can have kids share their writing in pairs and small groups.

Ultimately, the goal of the share conversation is not the conversation itself. All of the share sessions in this book are focused around conversations that improve both the students' writing products and their writing process. You'll see this unfold in a number of ways.

Many of the share sessions give kids opportunities to rehearse new writing ideas. Graves, defining rehearsal, said that it's the "preparation for composing and can take the form of daydreaming, sketching, doodling, making lists of words, outlining, reading, conversing or even

Don't Forget to Share: The Crucial Last Step in the Writing Workshop

writing lines as a foil to further rehearsal" (1983, 221). When I was a first-grade teacher, Danielle, one of my students, came to school clasping a napkin. On this napkin, she told me, were ideas she got for writing the night before while eating in a restaurant. She kept the crumpled-up napkin by her side for several days, and throughout the year she continued to bring in scraps of paper on which she had jotted brainstorms she'd gotten in restaurants, at the grocery store, and even on a visit to the dentist. That year, I wondered how to get all of my kids to rehearse their writing in the ways that Danielle and a few other kids like her did naturally. I now know the share is a perfect place to give everybody a chance to try this.

Other share sessions give students opportunities to *revise* their writing. Georgia Heard has said, "Revision involves changing the meaning, content, structure, or style of a piece of writing rather than the more surface changes that editing demands" (2002, 1). Many of your students might at times resist revision because they see it as an insult, rather than a natural and needed part of the writing process. Once again, the share is a perfect place for students to begin to see revision as an integral step.

Still other shares help kids discover their unique writing process. Calkins compares the writing process to the scientific method that researchers follow: "Just as researchers often follow a scientific method writers follow a process of craft when they work" (1994, 70). It's essential to realize that just as all researchers have a slightly different scientific method, so, too, all writers have a slightly different process. Some kids need to write in a quiet space, while others don't mind a little noise. Some kids need to reread and make changes to their writing at the start of every writing session, while others tend to do this toward the end. Some draw pictures to rehearse their ideas; others talk to a partner; still others make a quick outline. The truth is, not only is everybody's writing process different, but also each writer's process will change from piece to piece. The share session, as you'll see, can be a time for students to reflect on all of this.

Chapters 3 through 6 look at the types of share sessions in detail (Chapter 3, content shares; Chapter 4, craft shares; Chapter 5, process shares; Chapter 6, progress shares). Each of these chapters features a transcript of a share session in which you'll see the type of share in action. In the book I coauthored with Lucy Calkins, *Launching the Writing Workshop* (2003), we included transcripts of minilessons, fully

Figure 1.1 Overview of the Four Types of Share Sessions

TYPE OF SHARE	WHAT'S BEING DISCUSSED	HOW THE STUDENTS MIGHT PARTICIPATE	WHOSE WRITING PRODUCTS/ PROCESSES ARE BEING USED
Content	The content in one another's writing	• Share their writing • Retell and ask questions about their classmates' writing • Suggest revision ideas • Get revision or rehearsal ideas	A few (1–3) students' writing products
Craft	The craft in one another's writing	• Share craft techniques • Reread writing • Get revision or rehearsal ideas • Share craft ideas with partners	Everybody's writing product
Process	One another's writing process	• Share writing processes • Get writing process ideas	Everybody's writing processes
Progress	One another's writing progress	• Share and reflect on writing progress • Set new goals	Everybody's writing progress OR One person's writing progress

aware of and excited by the fact that people would try them out in their classrooms exactly as they were presented. The transcripts I've included in this book are helpful, but you will not be able to re-create them word for word, because every conversation unfolds in a slightly different way. I've included them so that you have a chance to see exactly what each type of share session looks and sounds like. Most important, I hope that seeing them helps you imagine how to orchestrate similar types of conversations in your own classroom.

To support this goal, I've organized each transcript similarly:

1. "Getting Ready" lists the materials that were used to enhance the conversation.

2. "Observations Before the Share" details the ways in which the teacher decided on the type of share she would lead, and then it explains why particular students were chosen to share.

3. The "Setup" describes how the teacher informs the kids about the type of share they'll be doing that day and why they're doing it. The teacher also uses this time to let the students know their roles and responsibilities.

4. The "Discussion" captures the kids having writerly conversations with one another. Interspersed in the discussion is my commentary, which points out how the teacher listened carefully to what the students were saying and then taught in direct response to it. I also name the teaching methods the teacher used, such as reinforcing, providing more than one example, and demonstrating, and provide tips on how to ensure that everyone is participating.

5. In "Future Teaching Ideas," each teacher shares how she'll continue teaching some of the concepts that arose in the share in future minilessons, conferences, and share sessions.

After each transcript, I reflect on the session in a section titled "The Special Power of Conversation." Here, you'll learn more about how the discussion helped the kids learn the concepts presented in the share in a more thorough manner. Additionally, Chapters 3, 4, and 6 have a section titled "A Close-in Look at Writing" that contains samples of students' writing that were affected by that particular share session.

Each chapter dealing with a specific type of share session concludes with sections designed to help you with your long-term planning and your day-to-day teaching:

1. "Planning Tips" suggests times in the year when you might conduct particular types of shares.

2. "Teaching Tips" offers practical advice on which types of students most benefit from the different shares.

3. "Additional Shares" lists some other possible share sessions you might conduct in your classroom.

It's been quite a challenge to apply some sort of organization to a type of teaching that is, at its best, often unpredictable. I hope these features help you strike a balance between embracing the wonderful spontaneity that's bound to occur in your share sessions and making sure these sessions are times during which all students can learn.

Share Meetings in Action

To give you an idea of what these writerly conversations look and sound like, let's listen to two of them.

First, we'll visit Marsha Childers' kindergarten classroom, in Prosser, Washington. It is late September, and she is finishing up her unit of study titled Launching the Writing Workshop. Marsha wants her students to get to know one another's favorite writing topics, so she decides to conduct a content share. Before the session Marsha has privately asked Julia if she will share her writing, and Julia has eagerly accepted the invitation.

Marsha: Today we are going to hear Julia's story about her dogs. First, I'll read Julia's story, and then afterward Julia will read it. That way you'll get a chance to hear her story twice. After we hear it, we'll make sure we understand it by retelling it to her. If there is anything that you're wondering about her story, just ask. I know that she'll be happy to help.

Marsha reads Julia's story with fluency and expression. Afterward, Marsha asks Julia to read it in the same manner.

Marsha: Let's make sure that we understand it. What happened first?

Don't Forget to Share: The Crucial Last Step in the Writing Workshop

A flurry of hands goes up.

Brad: One day Julia was playing with her dog Mo in her backyard.

Julia smiles and nods.

Marsha: And then what happened next?

Again, all the students raise their hands. Julia carefully scans the class and finally chooses Courtney.

Courtney: And then her neighbor came over with his dog Tinker.

Julia smiles and nods, clearly excited that her story has been understood.

Marsha: Julia, do we have your story right?

Julia: Yes.

Marsha: Now that we understand Julia's story, we can let her know if there is anything that we're wondering about. We're so lucky because we have Julia, the author, here to answer our questions. Turn to the person next to you and share what you're wondering about.

The students stop and talk, and then Marsha brings the class back together.

Christian: Were there any other dogs?

Julia: Yes, afterward, my grandma came with her dog Zoë.

Marsha: Let me see if I have your story straight. (*Marsha turns the pages of Julia's book, modeling the exact language that Julia can use later while writing the remainder of the story.*) "One sunny day I was playing with my dog Mo. Then my neighbor came with his dog Tinker." (*When Marsha gets to the last part of the story—the part Julia hasn't written—she points to a blank piece of paper.*) It's up to Julia, but who thinks it would make her writing better if she added what she said about her grandmother coming with her dog Zoë on to another page at the end? (*Marsha points once again to the blank page.*) What if she added "Afterward my grandmother came with her dog Zoë and all of the dogs played together"?

Most hands go up.

Marsha: What do you think, Julia?

Julia: I think I want to add that page.

Marsha: How exciting! Tomorrow you're not going to be starting a new piece. You're going to be revising this piece. *Revising* is a fancy word that means making your writing better. Look at how you all helped Julia by asking her if there were other dogs in her story. That helped

Julia think about what happened next and then add another page to her story. You can do the same thing. You can think about what happens next in your own stories and then add more pages. Thumbs up if you think that you might add another page to one of your stories to show what happened next, just like Julia did.

Next we'll visit Helen Yu's process share meeting with her third graders at PS 1, in New York City, in a February unit of study on the essay. During the day's writing workshop, Helen and I have noticed that the children are having trouble coming up with examples to use to develop their personal essays.

Helen: Today in our share session we're going to have a conversation about the types of examples we can use in our personal essays. We're having this conversation because some of you are having some trouble coming up with different types of examples. Please take a moment to prepare. How have you or might you come up with examples for your personal essays?

Helen gives the students a quiet moment to think.

Helen: Who wants to start the conversation?

Justine: I used my memory to go back to a time when I was playing with my cousin to show why I don't like her.

Helen: What is the main point of your essay?

Justine: That I don't like my cousin.

Helen: So you went back and used your memory to help you think about a time when your cousin did something that made you upset. This example supported your main point. Did anybody else do what Justine did? That is, did you try to remember an example that supports your main idea? Can you tell us about what you did, Michele?

Michele: I thought of a time when I saw a big kid being a trouble-maker in the playground, because my essay is about how big kids are troublemakers.

Helen: Many of you today went back into your memory to think about a time when this happened or that happened. It's like a small moment. But instead of writing a story, you are using these small moments as examples to support or show how your main point is true. Could everyone right now look back over your personal essay and see whether there's a place you could insert a story from your

Don't Forget to Share: The Crucial Last Step in the Writing Workshop

life to show how your main point is true? If there is, put a star there so you know that you can add that story later.

The students read over their writing, marking places where they could add stories to support their main point.

Helen: Did anybody do anything else other than use a story as an example?

Marcela: I thought about my mom and what she does every day. My essay is about how my mom is nice. I wrote down some of the nice things she does for me every day. She cooks me breakfast and she packs me my favorite snacks. These aren't things that just happened once. They happen every single day.

Helen: So what you're saying is that you think the examples in your essay could also be things that happen every day. It doesn't have to be just a onetime story. It could be something that happens a few times or regularly.

Marcela: Yes.

Kayla: Do the examples always have to be true?

Helen: What do you mean?

Kayla: Can you make up examples? My essay is about how best friends are great at keeping secrets. I have examples about times when my best friends did keep secrets, but one time my best friend didn't keep a secret. She told someone. Can I change that story and make it so she did keep the secret?

Helen: That's interesting. I don't think that we should change the truth in our personal essays, but your question brings up an interesting idea that I think we should talk about. We have a main point in our essays and we're for sure going to have some examples that support our main point, but we're also more than likely going to have some examples that go against our main point, like Kayla did. The question for us to consider is, What do we do with those examples? Do we include them? If so, how? Or do we just leave those examples out?

The students stop and think.

Bill: I think all of our examples should support our main point, because it will make our writing easier to understand. My essay is about how I think that there should be separate schools for boys and girls. All of my examples should be why I think that this is true.

A few students agree with what Bill has said.

Helen: Does anyone disagree?

Tatiana: Well, I think it will help people understand the point more if they see things that support it and that go against it. One problem with separate schools for boys and girls is that if you're always just with boys or always just with girls, you might not know how to get along with boys or girls when you grow up and get a job. I think that Bill should include this in his essay. It goes against his main point, but it's true. Like my main point is that there shouldn't be zoos. I have many examples to support my idea, but I can think of some that go against it.

A few students agree with Tatiana, and it is clear that this question still needs to be negotiated.

Helen: We'll keep talking about this in future share sessions, but for now, just so we can think more about Kayla's idea, reread your writing and imagine some examples that might go against your main point.

The students reread their writing.

Helen: There are a few ideas that came out of our share session today. One is that while writing personal essays, we can include a story that supports our big idea, like Justine talked about. We can also include something that happens all the time, like Marcela talked about. And Kayla helped us begin a conversation about what to do with the examples that go against our main point.

In my earlier days of teaching, I assumed a share was a quick way to bring the writing workshop to a close; I never gave it much thought. Now I see the share session much differently. I view it as an opening rather than a closing, a beginning rather than an ending. It is the perfect opportunity for us and our students to think, talk, and write together in more powerful and joyful ways. Minilessons and conferences are of course still valuable means by which to teach our students how to write well, but the share session lets kids engage in lively conversations—conversations that get them to linger over ideas and reflect on themselves and others as writers. What could be more powerful than that?

Listening and Speaking:
The Heart of the Share Session

The weaver carefully threads the first set of thread—the warp—
onto the loom. The warp gives the fabric its strength. Similarly,
a reading/writing program begins with listening, and listening
holds the program together.

—Jane Hansen, *When Writers Read*

Wouldn't it be great if you could just show up in class tomorrow and let your students know that from now on during share sessions, they are going to discuss important writing ideas with one another? And after you said that, these conversations would just magically happen? Unfortunately it's not that easy, as I quickly discovered during my first year of teaching.

I had high hopes that year of powerful share meetings, hopes of students having writerly conversations, hopes of facilitating these talks and then standing back and admiring my kids as they learned from one another. None of these things happened. In my shares, the students wiggled on the rug, looked at the clock, and counted down the minutes until lunch. Their comments or questions, when they made or asked them, were often just a means for talking about themselves. "I like your story about such and so; I do that too" was one of their favorite gambits. Other times, they responded in very formulaic ways, asking questions or making comments that they thought I would like but that in no way moved the conversation along.

The students sharing their work weren't much better. They usually spoke so softly that nobody could hear them, and when they did speak loudly enough, their struggle to read what they had on the page was often quite apparent. Usually I sat by silently, not sure how to intervene.

Looking back, I realize that those early shares didn't work because I didn't spend the time to make them work. Both teacher and student have responsibilities in a successful writing conversation.

The Listener's Role

Carol Avery, speaking about the listener's role in a share, says, "The writer has the easy part. We have the hard part. We must listen very carefully" (2002, 170). She's right. The listener does have a tough job, but, surprisingly, students tend to get more support in learning how to speak with one another than they do in learning how to listen to one another. So how do we go about helping our students become better listeners?

First, we need to draw children's attention to the importance of listening, not just in share sessions but throughout the day. I do this by showing kids a few active listening strategies, such as making eye contact with the person who is talking, leaning in toward that person, and nodding as a visual cue that you are paying attention. These strategies are a good beginning. Once the kids begin to understand these concepts, I move on to specific listening responsibilities that they can take on during a share session.

Understand What Was Written and Said

Comprehension is perhaps the most overlooked and most important part of a successful share conversation. Nodding one's head, making eye contact, and facing the speaker are all great listening strategies, but none of them can ensure that your students understand what they're hearing. When launching your share sessions, keep it simple: your main focus should be helping students understand one another.

Begin the year with content shares in which students read their writing aloud. Let the class know they should listen as carefully as they would during a read-aloud. After the student has finished, have the listeners try to *retell* the writing, remembering and using as many of the author's exact words as they can. In the beginning, you may model a portion of this retelling, but over time your kids should be doing the majority of it.

Don't Forget to Share: The Crucial Last Step in the Writing Workshop

As your kids get used to listening to one another, the retelling portion of the share will become shorter or perhaps disappear altogether.

Give and Get Ideas

Teachers often ask what they should do with students who seem passive during the share, who are engaged only when they are contributing ideas. This passivity occurs at least partly because the kids view the share as a time when they'll *give* ideas, not *get* ideas. You'll want to dispel this notion quickly, telling your students that in a share session they should be shopping for writing ideas every single day. I often ask my students at the end of a share, *"Who got an idea today that you think you'll use tomorrow?"* I say this because I want to reinforce the idea that they should be getting writing ideas every single day.

The Speaker's Role

There are many ways that students can talk during a share. By *speaker* here I mean the students who have been asked (or have volunteered) to share either their idea or their writing with their classmates.

Come Prepared

If you have an important meeting to attend and you know you'll be asked to contribute, you come prepared. Encourage your students to feel the same way: let them know that if they can prepare for the share meeting, they most certainly should. You can help by asking them to bring particular materials with them, such as their writing or a touchstone text. Or you might tell kids what they'll be talking about that day and then give them a quiet moment to gather their thoughts.

If students are going to be sharing their writing, they should prepare by reading it aloud beforehand, either to themselves or to a partner. There is nothing more embarrassing for the speaker or frustrating for the listener than for a student to stand in front of the class and be unable to read what he has written. Some students struggle reading their writing because they have drawn pictures, put down random strings of letters, or simply written illegibly. This is the perfect opportunity to point out tactfully why their writing is hard to read. You might ask younger students to "read" their picture rather than try to decipher the words they attempted to write.

Welcome Ideas

While sharing, students may come to realize that their writing or ideas could be revised, perhaps because of a suggestion from a classmate. This is a crucial moment: they can either be receptive to the suggestion or completely close down. Many students are not open to making changes, because they view it as evidence that their writing or ideas are flawed.

This is a good time to stress the point that writers regularly revise. To make it feel less permanent, I always assure kids that they can go back to their original thinking or writing if they end up not liking the new version. You'll also want to model your own revision process, showing the kids that when you revise you often discover what it is that you're really trying to say.

I say all of this with caution, however. Although I want students to be open to revision ideas, I don't want them to accept every suggestion. Peter Elbow (1993) speaks of the "gag order" prevalent in many writing workshops, explaining that students get feedback from their classmates or their teacher during a share, and then they're simply expected to make all of the suggested changes. Ultimately, students should be in charge of both their writing and their ideas.

The Teacher's Role

It's not just your students who have vital roles in the share conversation: so do you. I used to think I could watch my share sessions from afar, simply admiring my students in the midst of lively discussions. Although this sometimes happens, I now know that for the most part I have to orchestrate the sessions, albeit quietly.

Observe Students Before the Share

Some teachers tell me that in an effort to be fair, they take their class list and designate different days for different kids to share. This does make shares feel more manageable, but it doesn't give you the oppor-

Don't Forget to Share: The Crucial Last Step in the Writing Workshop

tunity to observe your students regularly and then decide the *type* of share you'll conduct on any given day and who (if anybody) will read their writing. This doesn't mean you shouldn't keep track of who has shared and make sure that over a period of time everyone gets a chance. It just means that you don't want to have a rigid schedule that gets in the way of your assessments.

You're going to have to decide each day which type of share your students will most benefit from that day. I make this decision by paying attention to what occurs in my minilessons and conferences, as well as by observing my students while they are writing. Figure 2.1 shows how I use what I see to decide what type of share I'll do.

Figure 2.1 Determining What Type of Share to Conduct

IF I SEE THAT . . .	THEN I MIGHT CONDUCT A . . .
There are students who are in the middle of a piece of writing and seem stuck. OR There are students who move quickly on to their next piece of writing with no thought of revision.	Content Share
Some students are resistant to my suggestions.	Content Share
Some students have few craft ideas.	Craft Share
Some students have tried out craft techniques I have introduced either in the minilesson or the conference.	Craft Share
Some students have tried some interesting craft techniques on their own.	Craft Share
Some students are having a difficult time working independently.	Process Share
Some students have tried some interesting strategies as part of their writing process (rereading, looking at the picture to help with the word, using a touchstone text when stuck).	Process Share
A student has made a major breakthrough in her writing	Progress Share

Once you know the type of share you're going to do, you need to decide who is going to share. If I've decided to conduct a content share, for example, I often (but not always) choose students who could use some extra help with revision. I do make sure, however, that during the year *all* students get an opportunity to have their writing featured in this sort of share. If I've decided to conduct a craft share, I choose students who have tried a technique that I would like others to try as well. Process shares are focused around everyone's writing process, so I don't need to choose a student on those days. If I'm conducting a progress share, I might feature a student or two who have made major breakthroughs in their writing, or I could also focus the conversation around everybody's progress.

Because my shares are based on my observations, I typically decide who will share rather than wait for student volunteers. I let the students know this early in the year so that they don't bombard me each day with requests. I also make sure that I ask each student privately if he wants to share. That way if a student is uncomfortable, he can let me know. If a child does say no, I may try to persuade her just a bit, but in the end I'll respect her decision.

Set Up the Share Session

Once you've observed your students and have decided on the type of share you're going to do, you'll want to ensure that everybody understands the purpose of the conversation. For example, I recently set up a process share in a fifth-grade classroom by saying, "Today I noticed that you guys were doing a lot of rereading, so I want to talk about how that helped or didn't help you. Listen carefully to one another's thoughts so that you can learn new ways to include rereading in your own writing process." This prompt helped students understand what they would be discussing and why. It also helped them understand what their role in the conversation would be. Figure 2.2 suggests possible setups for different types of shares.

Observe Students During and After the Share

Student voices should be prominent in share sessions. I sometimes have to remind myself to be quiet and observe. There are a few things I'm thinking about, though, while I'm observing. First, I'm watching to see if and when particular kids need my support. If I do feel they need

Don't Forget to Share: The Crucial Last Step in the Writing Workshop

Figure 2.2   Setups for Different Types of Shares

TYPE OF SHARE	POSSIBLE SET-UP
Content Share	Today we'll listen to a few kids share their "all about" books. We'll make sure we understand their writing by retelling it first. Then we'll think like a scientist and let the writer know what we're still wondering about.
Craft Share	Today during the minilesson I spoke about using descriptive language to describe your setting. A few students tried that today. I want you to listen to what they've done, because afterward you'll reread your writing to see if it could work in your piece.
Process Share	Today, we're going to discuss the ways that talking about your writing helps or doesn't help you. Take a moment to gather your thoughts.
Progress Share	Today José is going to share what happened when he found a quiet spot in the classroom to write. Let's listen so that we can talk about his progress and make goals for ourselves.

my help, I give them only a little, because I'd rather they do most of the work themselves. I'm also listening for concepts that arise that may need to be explored further on subsequent days in shares, minilessons, or conferences. I observe my students after the share as well, noting the impact that the share session is or isn't having on their writing.

Respond Immediately to What Students Say

The trick of a good share session is to listen to what students say and then make quick decisions about when and how you'll respond. This is very different from the way we teach in a minilesson. With minilessons, we observe our students over a couple of days, and then, based on our observations and our current unit of study, we carefully design a particular lesson. We take the time to plan not only what we'll teach but also how we'll teach it. For example, just recently I decided to do a minilesson with a second-grade class on including details about the setting. Once I decided on this topic, I carefully planned the words I would use to teach it.

In a share, however, we don't have time to plan what we'll teach or how we'll explain it to the kids. We have to respond immediately to what the kids say in the moment. This is similar to what we do when we confer with students, but the additional challenge here is that our quick responses should benefit not just one child but all children. How, exactly, do we go about doing that?

As a way to answer this question, let me explain what I was thinking while making quick teaching decisions during a recent share. Jesús was reading aloud what he had written about his grandma's surprise party. Afterward, Sheri said, "I like the part when you said there were balloons everywhere." I immediately jumped in, because establishing the setting was a class goal for this unit of study, and many students were not yet including setting details.

"You know, I'm wondering if maybe you like that sentence because he described what the place looked like. There is a special word for that. It's called *setting*." I pulled out a copy of *Fireflies* (Brinckloe 1985, 2). "Julie Brinckloe's book *Fireflies* reminds me of Jesús' writing. Both of them describe what the setting looked like. Listen to this: 'It was growing dark. My tree house was a black shape in the trees.' You guys can do what Jesús and Julie Brinckloe did: you can describe the setting."

To an outsider, this may have looked easy—as if I were making an offhand comment. But it was anything but. I would not have been able to respond nearly as well or as quickly to Jesús' comment if I hadn't known his teacher's goals for this unit of study. It also helped tremendously that I had a copy of *Fireflies* close by and that I knew the book well.

Throughout this book you'll find many examples of teachers making quick instructional decisions during share sessions. They make these decisions, as I did, by knowing their students, their goals for their unit of study, and the materials they have on hand.

Reinforce, Provide Examples, and Demonstrate

Once you've decided to respond to a particular comment, there are a few ways you can do it. First, you can *reinforce* what's been discussed by summarizing it. During a share in which students were discussing

Don't Forget to Share: The Crucial Last Step in the Writing Workshop

how rereading improved their writing, I reinforced their conversation by saying, "So far I heard Bill say that when he rereads he often discovers he forgot a word. Justine said that rereading helps her add new parts, and Jenny said that when she rereads it helps her locate misspelled words." In other words, I articulated a short, concise list of the important points that had been brought out. Later I also reinforced this discussion by linking it to the students' ongoing work, telling them that I hoped they would try some of these rereading strategies the next day.

You can also lift the level of learning by eliciting or providing additional *examples* of what's being discussed. In that same rereading share, every time a student shared a new strategy, I asked, "Did anyone else discover that today as well?" Then another child would share his experience with the strategy, thus giving the kids another example. You can also provide additional examples by referring to touchstone texts, as I did with Jesús.

You can also *demonstrate* different conversational moves. I do this carefully and sparingly, toward the end of the session. I watch students first, planning if and what I'll demonstrate based on the kids' needs. Just recently, in a first-grade classroom, Simone shared her writing about a fire in her house. In the story she wrote that her family was thrilled. I was dumbfounded, not understanding why her family would be happy that there was a fire. After Simone finished reading, I was dying to ask my question, but I held back, waiting to see whether any students had wondered the same thing. When no one responded, I decided to demonstrate a key conversational move: "Simone, I'm confused about one part of your story. You said your parents were thrilled. Why were they thrilled about a fire?" I heard whispered agreement from some of the students. Simone then explained that her family was thrilled because the fire didn't spread through the whole house. Her answer helped all of us understand her story better. Afterward, I told the students that if they were confused about something that someone wrote, they could let the writer know, just as I did.

Bring More Voices into the Conversation

Teachers often ask whether or not they should force quieter students to share. While I would never force a child who was dead set against sharing to do so, I do encourage those who, if it were left strictly up to them, probably wouldn't. I tactfully include them first in small ways and then in bigger ways. I'll often privately ask a quieter student to share; if she says no, I'll say, "I really wish you would. How about I read your piece and you just stand next to me as I read it?" Once a student agrees to this, she often becomes progressively more excited about participating, usually ending up doing much more than she originally said she would.

When I continually hear the same voices during classroom shares, I might say something like, "The same three kids keep sharing their ideas. Could everyone turn and share your thoughts with a partner?" or "Please take a moment to gather your thoughts. I know if you do, more of you will have ideas to share." I wait, and during those quiet moments I make eye contact with students who I hope will contribute.

Sometimes I'm very direct and ask students to share even when they have not indicated that they want to. Let me be clear here: I'm *not* doing this to catch someone who is not paying attention; rather, I'm doing it to pave the way for a student who is actively thinking during these meetings but is reluctant to share that thinking with others. I'm often pleasantly surprised at how this technique helps quieter students become more comfortable.

Ensure That the Share Session Is a Positive Experience for Everyone

Desiree Mains, a first-grade teacher, recently told me about a share meeting she had in which Carson, an extremely shy child, mustered up the courage to read his writing to the class. Desiree, of course, was overjoyed. After he finished, Carson proudly turned his writing around toward the kids. It was clear he had not used any spaces between his words. Justice innocently yelled, "I can't read it. His letters are all scrunched together." Hearing this, Carson literally crumbled, and Desiree knew that she had to do something quickly.

"You know, Justice, I bet you're dying to read Carson's story. Would it help if Carson added spaces?" Justice said yes. "I bet lots of you would love to read Carson's writing. Who thinks he could make this easier for you if he started to add spaces between his words?" Many hands went up. "Carson, look at how many people want to read your writing. You can help them by starting to leave some spaces."

This vignette highlights how Desiree took a potentially negative experience and turned it positive. In this book, I'm not talking only about shares in which we simply celebrate and honor students. I'm talking about ones in which we firmly push them to do more. Share sessions should help students like Carson begin to use spaces between their words, but we must address these delicate matters carefully.

You should teach your students to respond to one another in kind ways, but also keep in mind that they are young and at times unintentionally hurtful. Justice wasn't deliberately mean to Carson, but her words did wound, and it's our role in these situations to quickly reword the comments so that they can be used positively, just as Desiree did.

When I first started teaching I was filled with questions: *What do I do in the share meetings? What do my students do? And most important, how do I ensure that the share is instructive for everyone?* I now realize that the answers to these questions truly lie in the teacher's hands. Teach your students their roles in a share conversation, and make sure you understand your own role as well. When you do, you'll help your students not only as writers but also as thinkers, speakers, and listeners in the world.

3

Content Shares

Of all qualities, questioning is fundamental to being human. It is how we dispel confusion, probe into new areas, and strengthen our abilities to analyze and deduce.

–Ellen Keene and Susan Zimmermann, *Mosaic of Thought*

It was a sunny Tuesday morning and Beth Scammell's second graders were in the middle of a share meeting. Sandra was reading aloud her story about the day her younger brother broke his arm. "One day my little brother was sitting on a stool. A few minutes later, he fell off the stool and broke his arm." The rest of the story told what happened to her brother in the hospital and how the different family members reacted. Toward the end of her story came the statement "My dad was very, very sad, the saddest of us all!" I assumed I was getting the basic gist of the story, but I soon discovered I should have been questioning her text a bit more carefully.

Thank goodness the kids were listening more closely. After Sandra finished, Jake raised his hand and said tentatively, "There is a part of your story I don't understand. Where was your brother when he fell off the stool?"

Sandra answered, "He was in my dad's office. My dad had brought him to work with him."

The entire class had an aha moment. Shouts of "I thought your brother was at home" and "That's why your dad was the saddest of them all!" erupted from all corners of the classroom. Then Peter chimed in, "I bet your dad wasn't only sad. I bet he felt guilty."

Sandra's eyes lit up: "My dad felt really guilty because he left my brother alone on the stool while he did computer stuff."

After the share, Beth and I exchanged looks of amazement, not knowing which aspect to focus on first. We were thrilled that everybody (except me) had wondered where Sandra's brother was when he fell off the stool, and we were convinced that these kids would forever write with a better understanding of the importance of setting. We were pleasantly surprised that Jake, a student who lacked self-confidence, mustered up the courage to ask the all-important question that made Sandra, a very self-confident writer, realize she had left out an important detail. And of course we were excited that Jake's setting question and Peter's comment about feeling guilt enabled Sandra to more accurately match what she put on the page to what was in her heart. All of this came from a simple conversation about the content of one student's writing. Content shares help students question texts and gain a more thorough understanding of revision.

What Is a Content Share?

In a content share, one or two (perhaps three) students read their writing aloud. After each kid reads, the teacher asks the rest of the students to retell what they heard to make sure that everyone understands it. Then the kids ask for more information. Finally, the writer decides which parts of the discussion (if any) will help him revise the writing.

A Content Share in Action

It's October, and Beth Buchholz's second graders are in the middle of a personal narrative unit of study.

Getting Ready
- correction tape
- the special paper that the class uses to revise its writing

- the touchstone text *Shortcut*, by Donald Crews (1992)
- the writing of the student who is sharing

Observations Before the Share

Beth and I noticed that many students have finished one piece of writing and moved on to another. When we ask why, they say things like "I'm done" or "There is nothing else to write." We feel that their stories could be developed further but that the kids don't know how to do this. We decide to conduct a content share in the hope that the conversation will reveal some clear, concrete reasons to revise. After discussing whom we can ask to share, we pick Anthony, because he has resisted our revision ideas in the past and we hope he may be more open to ideas from his classmates. We ask him privately if he will share, and he says yes. He prepares by reading his writing to a partner before the share begins.

Setup

Leah: Today, Anthony is going to read his writing aloud. Afterward we'll retell it to make sure that we understand it. Then we'll ask Anthony anything that we're still wondering about. I'm sure he'll be happy to help us. I'll begin by reading Anthony's piece, and then Anthony will read it one more time. Notice that when I read his writing, I try to read it with the correct expression. I'm sure Anthony will do this as well.

I'm making sure students understand that their role in this share (as in any content share) is not only to understand the piece of writing but to speak up if and when they are confused.

Discussion

I read Anthony's piece, demonstrating reading with expression. This not only helps Anthony do the same when he reads but also lets him hear the beauty of his words. Sometimes, if I'm struggling to decipher what the student has written, I'll ask him to read first. Either way, the rest of the kids get to hear the story read properly twice, which helps them enjoy it as well as understand it better.

Leah: Let's retell Anthony's story to make sure we understand it. I'll start us off. One day Anthony went to Wal-Mart with his mom. Could you turn to the person next to you and continue the retelling?

Don't Forget to Share: The Crucial Last Step in the Writing Workshop

I have them do this in pairs to bring more voices into the conversation. It also ensures that all of the kids are attempting to understand Anthony's writing.

Leah: Who wants to continue the retelling?

Aileen: He bought a ghost sticker.

Leah: And then what happened?

Seymour: He had chocolate milk.

Caitlyn: He put the ghost sticker on the window to get ready for Halloween.

Leah: Anthony, did we get it right?

Anthony (*a big smile on his face*): Yes.

The best way to make our students feel like writers is to show them that we understand what they have written. Each time we retell a student's piece of writing, we build his writing identity in more ways than we can possibly imagine.

Leah: Is anybody wondering anything else about Anthony's story?

Teachers often tell me their students aren't ready to do this. My response is always: "Of course they are, as long as they have a beginning under-standing of what was read." I deliberately ask, "Does anybody want to know more about Anthony's story?" rather than "What questions or comments do you have for Anthony?" or "Let's give Anthony one compliment and one suggestion," to keep the kids directed toward the content. I have found that when I use those other wordings, students ask questions or make comments they think I'll like, rather than questions that help them better understand the writing.

Samantha: Did anybody go to Wal-Mart with you?

Anthony: My mom.

Bill: Did you buy anything else at Wal-Mart?

Anthony: Yes, a toy motorcycle.

Bridget: How did you get your mom to buy you a ghost sticker?

Anthony: When we were at the store, I said, "Mom, please, Halloween is coming. Can we buy a ghost sticker? It will make our house look so scary!"

Leah: What's your story mostly about?

I wait until near the end of the discussion to ask this question. I'll rein-force this conversational move very soon by saying, "Do you see how I asked, 'What's your story mostly about?' That might be a good question for you to ask when you're trying to better understand your classmates'

Figure 3.1   Questions Listeners Can Ask the Sharer

- What's the most important part of your writing?
- Can you say more about that part?
- What were you doing in that important part? (*character action*)
- What were you thinking about in that important part? (*character thought*)
- What were you saying in that important part? (*character dialogue*)
- Would you like to add what you just said into your writing?
- What kind of help would you like with your writing today?
- Is there a part in your writing that you would like us to listen to more carefully?
- What does _____ mean?
- What are you really trying to say?

stories." *(Figure 3.1 includes other questions you or your students might use in a content share to help students discover the focus of their writing.)*

Anthony: It's mostly about me being excited because it was close to Halloween and I was getting a ghost sticker.

Leah: I want to say again all of Anthony's answers to our wonderings. First, Anthony let us know that his writing was mostly about how excited he was that it was Halloween and that he was getting a ghost sticker. Anthony also said that he went to Wal-Mart with his mom and that while he was there he said, "Mom, please, can I get a Halloween ghost sticker? It will make our house look so scary!" He also said that he got a toy motorcycle. Anthony has lots of revision ideas, and now he has to decide which he wants to add. It's up to Anthony, but let's share with him what we think.

I'm doing two important things here. First, I'm reinforcing all the revision ideas by summarizing what has been said. I'm also slowing the conversation down by prompting the students to think about which ideas Anthony should add. This will help everybody develop a better understanding of revision.

Aileen: I think that he should add he went to Wal-Mart with his mom, because then people will know who he went with. If he doesn't add that, people might think that he was lost.

Leah: You think he should start his story by saying, "I went to Wal-Mart with my mom." You think he should include all the characters in that first sentence. That way, people will understand that he wasn't lost at Wal-Mart. Who thinks he should add that? (*Many hands go up.*)

Here, I imagine aloud exactly what Anthony's writing would sound like if he revised it to include all the characters. This approach is based on my recent observations of Anthony. At a different time or with a different kid, I might have given less support: "Anthony, why don't you imagine aloud what it would sound like if you revised your piece to include the characters?" Or, if I wanted to involve the whole class more directly, I might have said, "Everybody turn to someone near you and imagine aloud what Anthony's writing would sound like if he included all the characters."

Leah: What do you think?

Anthony: Yes, I want to add that.

Tony: He should add what he said to his mother. That was funny.

Leah: You think he should add the character dialogue. You think that he should add (*once again rehearsing the possible revision aloud*) "Mom, please, can you buy me a ghost sticker? Halloween is coming and it will sure make our house look scary."

Thomas: I think he should add that he got a toy motorcycle.

Leah: Now, remembering that his piece is all about being excited about Halloween, should he add the part about getting a toy motorcycle?

There is no way for me to predict whether the kids will recognize that this detail isn't related to the focus of his story. But I know that one of Beth's goals for this unit of study is focus, so I capitalize on this teachable moment.

Trish: I don't think he should, because that's not what his piece is about. It's about Halloween.

Leah: Are you saying that sometimes you don't add details because it doesn't go along with what your piece is about?

Trish: Yes.

Leah: Who agrees with what Trish just said? Sometimes you do add details because they go along with what your piece is mostly about, and sometimes you don't add details because they don't go along with what your piece is about.

As the students continue talking, it's clear this idea is still being negotiated. It is tempting just to tell the kids they should add only details that are important to the point of the story, but I know that more conversation is the only way they will truly come to understand this concept. I decide I will continue this conversation in future share sessions, minilessons, and conferences.

Leah: Anthony, what do you think? Do you want to add the part about getting a toy motorcycle?

Anthony: I'm not sure yet.

Leah: Why don't you think about it and then make a decision about it before writing workshop tomorrow?

In the end, Anthony makes his own revision decisions. Sometimes your kids will say yes to revision ideas, sometimes they will say no. Although I do keep my eye out for students who always say no, for the most part I respect their choices and remind myself that they benefit more from the conversation than they do from changing their writing. The inquiry that happens around student writing helps everyone see that behind every piece of writing is a reader trying to understand it.

Leah: We learned a lot from hearing Anthony's writing. We learned that it's important to let our readers know all the people or the characters in our story. Today and every day while you write you can also make sure that you add all of the characters into your own stories. We also learned that you can add dialogue to your stories. You can make the characters in your story talk to one another. We're still thinking about whether or not you should add any details you happen to think of or only those that are important to what your piece is about.

I reinforce the conversation by taking the revision ideas that students have suggested and making sure that everybody understands that these ideas can help them both rehearse new stories and revise their present ones.

Future Teaching Ideas

- Writers include all of the characters in their story.
- Writers ask themselves, "What is my story mostly about?"
- Listeners ask writers, "What is your story mostly about?"
- Writers add important details.
- Writers don't include unimportant details.
- Writers include meaningful dialogue.

The Special Power of Conversation

You just observed a share in which students talked about the content of one of their classmate's writing. Everybody was doing slightly different

Don't Forget to Share: The Crucial Last Step in the Writing Workshop

things, but everybody benefited. How did the act of discussion help engage kids in the instruction that was taking place?

1. ***They made important instructional decisions.*** Anthony was given several revision ideas to choose from and ended up using quite a few. I believe he made the revisions because he was given a choice, not told he had to. The whole class heard these ideas and had to decide which ones they would use immediately and which ones they would tuck away for another day. They also chose what they would ask Anthony. They were not given a list of questions. They asked questions based on what they did and did not understand.

2. ***They used their own language to explain complicated ideas.*** When the students were discussing the importance of including all the characters, Aileen offered a unique explanation of why this was important: if Anthony didn't put all of the people in his story, then the reader might think that he was lost. This was perfect seven-year-old reasoning. Beth told me that after this share session many kids began paying attention to the characters in their stories. I think Aileen's explanation helped bring this concept home.

3. ***They got to linger over ideas.*** Toward the end of the share I asked the kids, "Are you saying that sometimes you don't add details because it doesn't go along with what your piece is about?" At the beginning of the conversation many students thought that a good piece of writing had details everywhere, but by the end some were reconsidering their opinion. The conversation continued in future share sessions, which gave kids time to deepen their understanding and untangle some of their confusions. Eventually many kids changed their mind about the kinds of details good writing pieces have. What else could we want from a writing conversation?

A Close-in Look at Writing

To truly understand the impact content shares have on student writing, let's visit Dustie Zocher's first-grade classroom during her unit of study on writing how-to pieces. Anabell is reading her how-to piece aloud to her classmates. After she finishes, the other kids retell the piece to be sure they understand it. Then Tito shares something he is wondering about. Anabell has written, "Put the supplies away in the closet," and Tito wonders why someone would put a dirty broom next to all of the clean clothing in the closet. Anabell explains that the broom shouldn't go in the clothing closet; it should go in the kitchen closet. Because of Tito's question, Anabell decides to revise her writing and add the word *kitchen* (see Figure 3.2).

I like this example because it demonstrates how a revision as simple as adding one word not only improves a piece of writing but also helps kids understand the power of specificity. So often, we try to get kids to add big paragraphs when sometimes what they really need to understand is the power of one perfect word.

Figure 3.2   Anabell Revised Her Writing by Adding the Word *Kitchen*

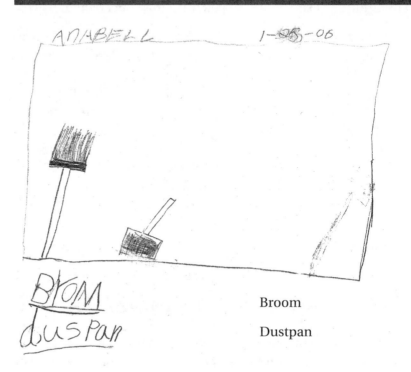

Broom

Dustpan

Don't Forget to Share: The Crucial Last Step in the Writing Workshop

Figure 3.2   Continued

1. gat the Brom ΣΕη You go.

2. Left and right in the flve Sep.

3. You got The dus Pan.

4. Σεn you swep The drt inTo The dusPan.

1. Get the broom. Then you go.

2. Left and right on the floor then.

3. You get the dustpan.

4. Then you sweep the dirt into the dustpan.

Figure 3.2   Continued

5. Then you put the dirt into the garbage.

6. Put the supplies away into the kitchen closet.

Planning Tips: When Should You Conduct Content Shares?

Content shares are powerful anytime during the year, and you'll want to conduct them from fall through spring. But here are some specific times when they're especially beneficial:

1. **At the start of the year.** Content shares work well at the start of the year for a number of reasons. First, they build community: students to get an opportunity to know one another through the

topics and ideas they share. The start of the year is also when you're trying to help your kids get better at speaking and listening to one another, not just in shares but throughout the entire day. In Beth's classroom, the listeners needed to be sure they understood what was shared, and the speakers had to read in a voice loud enough for others to hear. These listening and speaking strategies are building blocks for other literacy activities, as well as other types of share sessions.

2. *During a revision unit of study (or the revision phase of a unit of study).* Many teachers include a revision unit of study in their curriculum. These minilessons and conferences are supported by content shares that highlight the revision that is taking place. Many teachers also teach revision as part of *each* unit of study. It's helpful to conduct content shares *right before* students revise their writing.

3. *At the same time you teach students to question the texts they read.* In both share sessions described in this chapter, revisions took place when students questioned one another about their writing. Questioning is certainly an important strategy to use during content shares, but it's also an important strategy students should use when reading. Many teachers I work with conduct content shares *at the same time* they're working with kids on questioning the books they read. They make this connection crystal clear by saying something like, "In shares we listen to our classmates' stories more than one time and that helps us realize what we're still wondering about. You'll want to do something similar when you're reading a book. You'll want to read parts of the text more than one time, asking, 'What am I still wondering about?'"

Teaching Tips: Which Kids Benefit Most from Content Shares?

Everybody benefits from a content share. However, content shares work especially well with particular students' strengths and needs:

1. ***Students who resist revision.*** Students who resist your revision ideas are great kids to ask to read their writing during content shares, because they're often more open to revision ideas from their classmates. Once several students have suggested revisions, you might imagine these ideas aloud (as I did with Anthony), so that making the changes feels easier to do. You'll also want to get these students involved in retelling other students' writing by saying things like, "Barb, can you start us off?" or "Juan, can you continue the retelling?"

2. ***Students who don't question the texts they read.*** Some students read books quickly, never stopping to think or wonder about what they're reading. Share sessions in which they question their classmates' pieces of writing prompt these students also to question the texts they read. This type of questioning is usually easier in share sessions than during independent reading, because their classmates' topics are usually familiar; they also don't have to worry about reading the words. When I notice these students wondering about their classmates' writing during content shares, I show them how the wondering work they just did connects with the wondering work I want them to do while reading.

Additional Shares

The content shares you conduct in your classroom will be the result of what your students say and do on any given day, so it's impossible to give you a list of all the types of content shares. Instead, the following table on page 45 shows you some examples of content shares that might arise in your classroom, along with the language you and your students might find helpful during your discussions.

Speaking about revision, Toni Morrison has said, "The absolutely most delicious part is finishing it and then doing it over. That's the thrill of a lifetime for me" (1998, 200). How do we help our students see revision as a thrill of a lifetime rather than a task they dread? Use your share meetings to get kids thinking and wondering about one another's writing and before you know it, they'll be chomping at the bit to finish their writing and then start making it better.

DIFFERENT TYPES OF CONTENT SHARES	HELPFUL LANGUAGE FOR THE LISTENER TO USE
Students wonder about the focus in a classmate's writing.	What's the most important part?
Students wonder about the confusing parts of a classmate's writing.	I don't understand the part when . . .
Students wonder about the missing parts in a classmate's writing.	Could you say more? What does that mean? What happened next? Is there a part that you didn't write about? What happened before? What did it look like? What did it sound like? What did it feel like? What did your sister say? What did she do? What were you thinking?
Students wonder about the audience of a classmate's writing.	Who are you writing this for? What do you want the reader to understand after reading this?

Content Shares at a Glance

What is a content share?	In a content share, one or two (perhaps three) students read their writing aloud. After each kid reads, the teacher asks the rest of the children to retell what they heard to make sure that everyone understands it. Then the kids ask for more information. Finally, the writer decides which parts of the discussion (if any) will help her revise the writing.
When should you conduct content shares?	• At the start of the year • During a revision unit of study (or the revision phase of a unit of study) • At the same time you're teaching students to question the texts they read
Which students benefit most from content shares?	• Students who resist revision • Students who don't question the texts they read

Craft Shares

> When students are taught to see how writing is done, this way of
> seeing opens up to them huge warehouses of possibilities for how
> to make their writing good writing.
>
> —Katie Wood Ray, *Wondrous Words*

After reading *Wondrous Words* (Wood Ray 1999), I was more aware than ever that in order for kids to write well, they need not only a good topic but also lots of ways to write about that topic. Katie Wood Ray's book taught me the importance of teaching craft on a regular basis, and after I finished reading it I chose some touchstone texts I could use to teach craft in my minilessons and conferences. I was amazed at how dramatically this teaching affected my kids' writing, and now I can't imagine teaching any other way.

You probably already use touchstone texts to teach craft in your minilessons and conferences, but kids can also learn about craft by having conversations about it during share sessions. During these discussions kids are not just talking about the craft in touchstone texts but also discussing the craft in one another's pieces of writing.

What Is a Craft Share?

In a craft share, one or two (perhaps three) students share a technique they have tried in their writing. Then the rest of the students either reread their present piece of writing, imagining what it would sound like if they revised it using this technique, or rehearse how they might use the technique in a future piece. Either way, students document their new craft ideas so they can refer to them during future writing workshops. Finally, they share their ideas, first in pairs and then as a class.

A Craft Share in Action

Ellen McCrum is conducting a nonfiction unit of study in her fifth-grade classroom. She has been talking about craft with her students since the start of the year, so she uses the word *craft* freely and the students understand exactly what she means.

Getting Ready

- Sticky notes
- Two nonfiction touchstone texts: *Pigs, Pigs, Pigs*, by Gail Gibbons (1999), and *Should There Be Zoos: A Persuasive Text*, by Tony Stead et al. (2002)
- Pencils
- Clipboards
- Every student's current piece of writing

Observations Before the Share

During the last few minutes of writing workshop, Ellen has noticed that most of the students have no problem choosing what to write *about* (topics) but many are unsure *how* to write about the topics they have chosen (craft). Therefore, she decides to conduct a craft share. She privately asks Chantal and Darien if they will share, because each student has tried an interesting technique that she thinks will benefit a wide range of writers. Chantal and Darien prepare by rereading their writing aloud and thinking about how they will explain what they've tried to do.

Setup

Ellen: Today I've chosen Chantal and Darien to share, because they've tried some interesting craft techniques in their writing pieces. I want you to listen to see if what they did gives you ideas for what you can do. I've given each of you a couple of sticky notes so that you can write these ideas down.

Ellen reminds her students that it's their responsibility to listen to the techniques that are shared and then try them out.

Discussion

Ellen: Chantal, why don't you go first? (*Chantal reads her piece. Ellen quickly retells it to be sure the class understands.*) Chantal, will you share some of the craft that you used today?

Chantal: I used headings. (*She holds up her paper and points to her headings.*) On my first page I made this question dark. It's my heading. It says, "What do horses look like?" All the words after that heading are going to be about what horses look like. My heading will help readers understand what the next part is going to be about. Next, I made another part of my writing dark because it's my next heading. It says, "What do horses eat?" I haven't finished this part, but my plan is that the words after this heading will be all about what horses eat.

Ellen: How did you decide what your different headings would be?

Chantal: I thought about my topic, which is horses, and I asked myself, "What's most important about that topic?" In my head I answered the question. I thought that some of the most important information about horses was what they looked like and what they ate. That is why I made those my headings.

Ellen demonstrates an important conversational move by asking, "How did you decide what your different headings would be?" She wants the students not just to know that Chantal used headings but to understand how she went about doing so. She hopes students will begin asking one another this question as well.

Ellen: Chantal used headings in her nonfiction, and she created those headings by asking, "What's most important about my topic?" I'd like the rest of you to give this a try. Please reread your writing and ask yourself, "What's most important about my topic?" On a sticky note, write down some of your possible headings. After you've done this, turn to a partner and share.

The kids now have a chance to make plans on their sticky notes for future writing sessions. What an important strategy for students to learn! I often jot down notes about my drafts just as they're doing here. These notes help me write on future days with more clarity and intention.

Ellen: Let's have a few students share how they might use headings in their writing.

Don't Forget to Share: The Crucial Last Step in the Writing Workshop

Doug: My piece is about baseball, but I think I'll use headings like Chantal did. My headings might be "Positions in Baseball," "Rules of Baseball," and "How to Prepare for a Baseball Game."

Ellen: Great. Make sure that you get those headings down on your sticky note so you don't forget them. Anybody else?

Doreen: My piece is about cats. I'm going to use headings also.

Ellen: What might the title of your headings be? What do you think is the most important information about cats?

Here, Ellen moves Doreen along from simply saying she will use headings to helping her think aloud about what the words in those headings might be. It's easy to say that you'll try something, but it's more likely to happen if you actually practice the words aloud as Ellen asks Doreen to do.

Doreen: My headings might be "What does a cat look like?" "What does a cat eat?" and "What do you do if your cat gets sick?"

Ellen: Great; write those ideas down on a sticky note. Now let's have Darien share. Darien, will you read your piece and then let us know some of the craft techniques that you tried?

Darien reads, and then Ellen quickly makes sure that the students understand what he has written.

Darien: I made sure that I had a big idea, and then underneath that big idea I gave the readers specifics about my topic. Like here, I said, "Dogs eat many types of food." That's my big idea. Underneath the big idea, I gave the reader specific examples of the types of foods that dogs eat. I said, "Dogs eat dog food. In some households, people feed their dogs human food such as steak, hamburgers, and chicken."

Remember, Darien prepared beforehand what he would say.

Ellen: Do you see what Darien did? He had a big idea, *dogs eat many types of food*. And then after that big idea he helped the reader by providing specifics about that big idea. Our book *Pigs, Pigs, Pigs* reminds me of Darien's writing. Look. (*Ellen reads a page.*) "There are about three hundred different breeds of pigs, but all pigs have the same basic characteristics." There is Gail Gibbons' big idea, and then underneath the big idea she gives some specifics, just like Darien did. She says, "They have a heavy, round, bristly-skinned body with a round, flat nose called a snout."

Ellen's decision to use Pigs, Pigs, Pigs *looks seamless, but it's the result of a lot of smart thinking and planning. She can't refer to that touchstone text unless it is right there by her side. She also knows it well. If we want to take advantage of all the teachable moments in our share sessions, we must take seriously the admonition that our materials must be nearby and we must know them inside and out. Ellen is also able to make this quick teaching decision look easy because she knows her students well. Because many of the kids are having problems including both big ideas and specifics in their writing, she deliberately slows the conversation down. Ellen also uses the book in a very insightful way. She doesn't begin the way she typically might have: "Let's write like Gail Gibbons." Rather, she begins with Darien's writing and shows how Gail Gibbons writes just like Darien. It's an interesting twist on how to use a touchstone text.*

Ellen: Some of your writing pieces have big ideas, but they don't have many specifics. You say something like dogs eat many things, but then you don't write enough about the specific things that dogs eat. Some of you have the exact opposite problem. You have lots of specifics, but you don't let your readers know what the big idea is. You write, dogs eat dog food, dogs eat steak, but nowhere do you say what all of those sentences are about. You'll want to make sure that you have both big ideas and specifics in your writing, just like Darien and Gail Gibbons did. I'm going to have you reread your writing as you think about this. Look for places where you think you might have to add either a big idea or perhaps some more specifics. On your second sticky note, write down some of these plans.

The kids begin working.

Ellen: Did anyone realize you had to add a big idea to your writing?

Sam: Yes, in my writing I said, "Some people like to learn salsa dancing and others enjoy learning ballet." I also wrote about tap dancing, and how that's a fun type of dance to learn as well. I think I need to add something in my writing about how in the world there are many different types of dances that people are interested in learning about.

Tory: Sam, how did you come up with that big idea? I can't figure out mine.

Sam: Well, I looked at all of the dancing sentences and asked, "What are these sentences mostly about?" Then I tried to answer the question. They were mostly about the different dances that people in the world are interested in learning. The answer to that question became one of my big-idea sentences.

Notice how Tory tries out the same conversational move that Ellen used earlier.

Don't Forget to Share: The Crucial Last Step in the Writing Workshop

Ellen: What Sam just said might help some of you when you are trying to figure out some of your big-idea sentences. You might do what Sam did. You might reread, asking yourself, "What are all my sentences about?" Is there anyone else who had the big idea but realized that you needed to add some specifics?

Courtney: Yes, I said, "Buildings come in many shapes and sizes," but I didn't give any examples of buildings. I'm thinking that I'm going to include some information about tall buildings such as skyscrapers and some smaller buildings such as shops and bodegas.

Ellen: What a great conversation. I want to remind you of the two big ideas that we talked about. First Chantal showed us how to use headings in our writing. Then Darien reminded us of the importance of including both big ideas and specifics. Let's take five minutes right now to try out some of these new craft techniques in our writing.

Sometimes I give students a few minutes after the share to try out some of the craft ideas, just as Ellen does here. Some students find this extremely helpful, while others are just exhausted and would be better off trying them fresh the next day. You'll decide what works best in your classroom on a given day.

Future Teaching Ideas

- Writers use headings to organize similar information.
- Writers asked themselves, "What that are most important things about my topic?"
- Writers have a big-idea sentence (or sentences).
- Writers create big-idea sentences by rereading their writing and asking, "What are these sentences mostly about?"
- Writers include specifics that go along with their big-idea sentences.

The Special Power of Conversation

Many of us teach craft throughout writing workshop, but in share sessions students get an opportunity to talk about their craft with one another in a way they may not be able to do during minilessons and conferences. In the previous share session, how did the students benefit from learning about craft techniques through conversation?

1. ***They made important instructional decisions.*** The students talked about and tried out more than one craft technique, but eventually they made their own decision about which ones they would integrate into their writing. This concerns some teachers. They feel students should be required to use all of the techniques discussed. I worry that if we require kids to do this, they'll become passive and integrate techniques not because they believe doing so will improve their writing but because they know it will please their teacher. When we let kids decide for themselves, we give them an important opportunity to reflect on their writing and figure how to make it better.

2. ***They used their own language to explain complicated ideas.*** In the past when my kids tried new craft techniques in their writing, I had them stand next to me as I explained what they had done, because I worried they would be unable to give a clear explanation on their own. At times, our students do need our help in explaining things, but we lose out when we don't have students explain complicated writing ideas to one another in their own unique, child-friendly ways. Both Darien and Chantal planned beforehand how they would explain what they tried in their writing to their friends. This not only helped them better understand what they had done but also allowed them to give their classmates simple explanations for more complicated concepts.

3. ***They got to linger over ideas.*** Ellen deliberately slowed the conversation down so that every student had time to internalize the techniques that had been introduced. First, she had Darien and Chantal name what they did. Then, she asked the rest of the kids to reread their writing, imagining what it would sound like if they tried the same thing. Next, the kids shared their ideas with a partner. Finally, they discussed their ideas as a class. Ellen also had the students document these plans so that this thinking could continue even after the conversation was over.

A Close-in Look at Writing

To see the impact that craft shares have on student writing, let's visit Millie DeStefano's first-grade classroom during their Small Moment unit of study. When Millie observed her students, she noticed that many of their stories were bare-boned and included mostly plot. She decided to conduct a craft share so they could talk about the types of details to include in their stories. One of the kids had included a character's feelings. After he shared this technique, Millie asked the other students to reread their writing and put a star in places they could imagine trying something similar. In Figure 4.1, Jet marked two places in her writing where she wanted to add character thinking. The next day she returned to her writing and did just that:

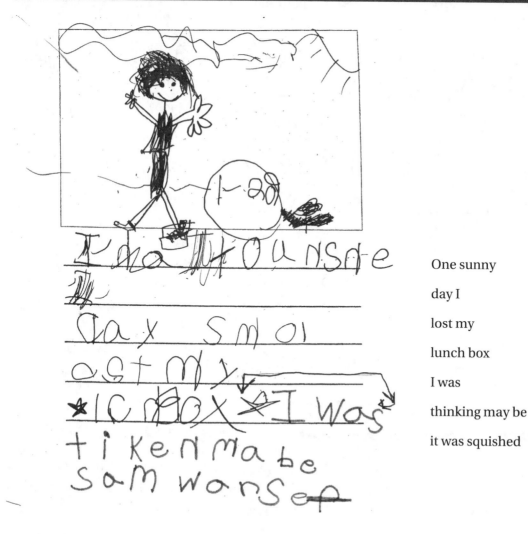

One sunny

day I

lost my

lunch box

I was

thinking may be

it was squished

Figure 4.1 Continued

I WaS PoX+Sen
MY VaW IS
ta go ~~bou~~ + i~
AeIOUand2M
+IMS ~~X~~ I Was
VereuaSet

I was practicing

my vowels,

a, e, I, o, u, and sometimes *y.*

I was

very upset."

Planning Tips: When Should You Conduct Craft Shares?

Our students can never have enough craft conversations! Each one will improve their writing just a bit more. But here are some particularly good times in the year to have a craft share:

1. *During the immersion phase of a unit of study.* During this phase, students are studying the types of texts they're about to write. Craft shares are a perfect way to help kids understand that the purpose of immersion is to rehearse future writing ideas. Students can discuss the craft techniques in the books they're studying and then imagine what their future writing would be like if they tried the same things.

2. *When students don't have many craft ideas.* Sometimes kids reach a plateau in their writing. They aren't pushing themselves to try out new things. This is a great time for students who are trying new techniques to push the others to take more risks.

3. *When you have recently introduced a new craft technique in a minilesson or conference.* When you teach a minilesson on craft and only a few kids try what you have taught, you can use a craft share to help more kids understand how to use the technique in their writing. For example, if I have presented a minilesson on different ways to end a story, I might have students who have tried different endings share their work. You can also use a craft share to show all the kids a specific technique you have shown one student in a conference. I do this when I think the technique I taught one child will benefit most of the others.

Teaching Tips: Which Students Benefit Most from Craft Shares?

As you conduct craft shares in your classroom, you'll zero in on particular students because the conversation is *exactly* what they need to become more independent and confident writers.

1. *Students who have a tough time getting started.* Teachers often ask how they can help students who continually struggle to get going on their own. Craft shares are a perfect tool, because they are designed to help kids plan their future work. I watch these

students as they make their plans during the share and then say something like, "Now you have a plan for tomorrow's writing workshop." I write down their plan as well, so I can remind them the following day if they've forgotten.

2. *English language learners.* English language learners are doing two things at once during writing workshop: trying to learn more about how to write well while at the same time trying to learn more about the English language. Craft shares prompt these students to rehearse their ideas orally before they write them down. During a craft share, I support my English language learners by saying something like, "Let's practice what your writing would sound like if you used character action. I'll start you off," and then let them continue rehearsing what they're going to write. I then have them practice the whole idea one more time: "OK, let's put it all together. Tell the whole story one more time." You'll want these kids immediately to write down what they said while it's still fresh in their mind.

Additional Shares

There are many types of craft shares you can conduct in your classroom, and it's impossible to give you a comprehensive list. Instead, here is a sample of the types of craft shares that may crop up in your classroom, followed by language you can use during the discussions. You can add your own ideas to these lists as you identify your students' unique strengths and needs.

Different Types of Craft Shares

1. Immersion: What ideas did you get from reading nonfiction today that you might use while writing nonfiction tomorrow?

2. Building the World of Your Character: When you're writing realistic fiction you'll want to make sure that you include character action, character thinking, and character dialogue.

Don't Forget to Share: The Crucial Last Step in the Writing Workshop

3. Exposure to Genre: What types of genres or forms (letter, list, card, book review, etc.) did you try today? Who thinks you might try one of these genres or forms tomorrow?

4. Using Questions: Who thinks you might ask a question in your writing tomorrow?

Helpful Language to Use During a Craft Share

1. Could you explain what you did in your writing?

2. How did you do that?

3. Can you go back and reread your writing, imagining where you could use the same craft that _____ used?

4. What would it sound like if you tried it? Try practicing the exact words to a partner.

5. Can you go back and reread your writing and put a star where you could use that same craft?

6. Write your idea on a sticky note and make sure you have it near you tomorrow while you're writing.

7. Take a moment right now to add these ideas to your piece of writing.

8. Don't forget to use these ideas when you write tomorrow.

What a difference it has made in my teaching to understand the power of craft and know that I can teach my students about craft not just in minilessons and conferences but in share sessions as well. In share conversations we can truly show all of our students how to talk with one another, imagining their way into beautifully crafted writing.

Craft Shares at a Glance

What is a craft share?	In a craft share, one or two (perhaps three) students share a technique they have tried in their writing. Then the rest of the students either reread their present piece of writing, imagining what it would sound like if they revised it using this technique, or rehearse how they might use the technique in a future piece. Either way, students document their new craft ideas so they can refer to them during future writing workshops. Finally, they share their ideas, first in pairs, then as a class.
When should you conduct craft shares?	• During the immersion phase of a unit of study • When students don't have many craft ideas • When you have recently introduced a new technique in a minilesson or a conference
Which students benefit most from craft shares?	• Students who have a tough time getting started • English language learners

Process Shares

Teachers can invite, facilitate, motivate, support, and direct but unless students learn—and learning requires the participation of learners—teachers can't really claim that any teaching has occurred.

—Lynn K. Rhodes and Curt Dudley-Marling,
Readers and Writers with a Difference

In the preceding chapters, you've seen how the talk that students do during share sessions dramatically improves the quality of their writing. It's safe to say, then, that it's wise to have students talk before they write. And if talking improves writing, what about the opposite: does writing improve talking? I think it does, and so does Thomas Newkirk. In his book *More Than Stories*, he says, "Writing can just as easily and profitably be viewed as pretalk" (1989, 153).

What Is a Process Share?

In a process share, the teacher poses a question that pertains to the writing process: What do you do when you don't know how to spell a word? What do you do when you don't know what to write about? The kids may or may not bring their writing with them, depending on what they will be talking about. Then the kids explore the question, using all of their prior writing experiences to help them.

A Process Share in Action

It's the first few weeks of school, and Lisa Cowan's kindergartners are just becoming comfortable writing stories from their lives, putting them down any way they can.

Getting Ready

- Several kinds of paper
- Two touchstone texts: *The Snowy Day*, by Ezra Jack Keats (1962), and *The Pigeon Finds a Hot Dog*, by Mo Willems (2004)
- Every student's current piece of writing

Observations Before the Share

Lisa and I have noticed that after about ten minutes of writing, kids jump up and declare that they are done. Therefore, we've decided to conduct a process share, our goal being to help students write for a longer time. Since the conversation will be focused around everyone's writing process, there is no need to choose a child to share.

Setup

Leah: Writers, I brought everyone together today for a special share. I was so proud of you as I watched you write stories all by yourselves. Congratulations! Many of you, after a little while, had a problem. You were done, and you weren't sure what to do next. Let's try to solve this problem together. In writing workshop we're going to write until the bell goes off. What can you do when there is more writing time, but you think you're done? Close your eyes and take a quiet moment to think. Then we'll talk about it together.

I let students know that their job is to come up with ideas on how to write for a longer time. It is implicit that they should not suggest things like "Go to the block area" or "Finish up math fractions." The question you ask needs to be clear and focused so the discussion doesn't go in a direction that you would rather it not.

Don't Forget to Share: The Crucial Last Step in the Writing Workshop

Discussion

Leah: Who wants to start us off? What can we do to help ourselves write for a longer time?

Tony: You can write words. I have my story about the day I went on a car trip with my family. I drew everything that happened in my story. Now I could write, "I went on a car trip with my family."

Leah: Just like real books. (*I hold up the book* The Snowy Day.) This book has pictures just like Tony's book does, but it also has words. The picture is at the top, and the words are at the bottom. You're right, Tony. So tomorrow if you think you're done, you could add words to your pictures, couldn't you? You could put the picture at the top and the words at the bottom, just like Ezra Jack Keats did. There is also another way that you guys could try out Tony's idea. Look at this book. (*I pull out* The Pigeon Finds a Hot Dog.) In this book there are words right in the picture. (*I show them an appropriate page.*) Who thinks you might try Tony's idea of putting down words? (*Almost everybody's hand goes up.*) If you do add words, you'll have to decide whether you'll add words like Ezra Jack Keats did, at the bottom of the page, or like Mo Willems did, right in the picture. (*As I say this, I once again point to a place in the respective book that shows what the particular approach looks like.*)

This is the first month of kindergarten! Can they all really add words to their pictures? Whether your students are five or fifteen, they need to approximate in order to write for longer periods of time. Although many of these students cannot write conventionally, they certainly can approximate writing letters and words. In kindergarten, the teachers tend to be more nervous than the students about putting print on the page. I've found that if I invite kindergarten kids to do so, they happily accept the invitation and write words the best they can. I'm also prepared for this share meeting. I have both of April's current touchstone texts with me. I have read them both and thought about ways to use them. As the students talk, I lift the conversation by providing concrete examples. I am also aware of April's present and future goals, and I can teach to them when it makes sense. I know that one of April's goals for this Launching the Writing Workshop unit of study is to get kids comfortable using both pictures and words. Therefore, I slow down the conversation when Tony brings it up.

Leah: Any other ideas? (*I take a moment to glance around the circle.*)

Tanya: You could start a new book.

Leah: What do you mean?

Tanya: Well, if I write one book about playing at the park with my sister, when I'm done I could write the story of Crystal's birthday party.

Leah: So, you mean (*I hold up two blank booklets*) that if you write one story and you're done, you could get another booklet to write your next story. What a great idea! Who thinks you might try Tanya's idea tomorrow? Who might start a new story? (*A flurry of hands goes up.*)

I have talked about this with Tanya earlier; after our conference I asked if she would share that idea with the class, and she said yes. I'll often ask a student to share an idea we've discussed in a conference.

Leah: Do you see this very special paper I have? (*I point to the blank booklets.*) Some of you might decide to use these books to write your stories in.

One of April's goals for her next unit of study is to introduce some new paper choices. I often use the share as a place to jump-start future goals, but again, I can do this only if I know what those goals are.

Leah: Any other ideas?

Matthew: You could just take a little rest.

Leah: Matthew, you did work really hard today, and I bet you did feel like you could use a little rest. One thing we're trying to do this year is to strengthen our writing muscles. If you feel like you need a little rest, then go ahead and take one, but then you'll want to quickly keep on writing so that you get nice, strong writing muscles.

I know that Matthew isn't being provocative but honest. He's four. I respond by validating where he is but moving him forward as well.

Leah: I have an idea. Couldn't you also reread your pictures and words and ask, "Is there more I can add"? Couldn't Crystal, before she starts her new story, reread her pictures and ask, "Can I add more"? Would you all give that try right now? Reread your writing and ask yourself, "Can I add more?"

The kids reread their writing.

Crystal: I forget to draw the part of my story when I was on the slides and swings. After I went on the monkey bars, I slid down the slide and played on the swings with my brother.

Leah: If you drew that part of your story, it would help people understand it more. Look at what Crystal could do. She could turn her

Don't Forget to Share: The Crucial Last Step in the Writing Workshop

story into a book by adding another page about playing on the slide and the swings. Maybe she'll draw the picture. Maybe she'll write the words. Maybe she'll do both.

Crystal: I want another page for my story!

Leah: Did you hear that, everyone? Crystal's book could have more pages just like a real book. If you want to make a book, you could take a booklet like I showed you before, or you could just get more pages like Crystal is going to do.

Sometimes I move the conversation along by adding my own idea at the end. In this case I know there are some students who are ready to reread but won't do it unless they get a little nudge from me. I extend my rereading invitation to everyone by letting the students know they can reread either their pictures or their words.

Leah: So we had three ideas today about what you can do when you think you are finished. One, you can add words. Two, you can start a new story. And three, you can reread and add more pages to the story you're working on. Take a moment to talk to the person next to you, letting him or her know what you think you'll do tomorrow when you're done and there's still more time left.

Writing conversations always get me revved up to try new things: I can't generate that kind of enthusiasm on my own. This is true for kids too. April's students practically jump for joy as they talk with one another about what they will do tomorrow when they think they are finished. They can't wait to write longer stories, try out words, and reread their writing! I take notes throughout the entire conversation so that later on I will be able to create a class chart titled "What Can We Do When We Think We're Done?" (Because this is a kindergarten class, the chart will include both pictures and words.)

Future Teaching Ideas

- Writers add different types of details to their pictures (setting, characters, characters' expression, characters' actions).
- Writers carefully use the stapler to put the pages of their story together.
- Writers put words in their pictures in lots of different ways (thought bubbles, dialogue bubbles, labels).
- Writers look at their picture to help themselves write words.

- Writers stretch their words out, listening carefully to the beginning, middle, and ending sounds.
- Writers do the best they can when they come to a word or a part of a word that they don't know.
- Writers put spaces between their words.
- Writers use their finger when rereading their writing.

The Special Power of Conversation

Weren't you in awe of the way April's students talked about their writing processes? They were able to talk so beautifully about the topic because they had just finished writing. Whenever I demonstrate a process share, teachers comment that what the kids talked about is exactly what they had planned to teach next in a minilesson. The more process shares teachers conduct, the fewer minilessons they have to do on those topics. The share session in April's classroom gave students the unique opportunity to *talk* about their processes, rather than be told or shown what those processes should look like

1. *They made important instructional decisions.* The students had two opportunities to make important decisions. First, they chose what would be discussed—that is, they came up with the various ideas about what they could do to write for a longer time. Second, they chose which ideas would work best for them. If we want all of our kids to achieve the same goals then we need to provide them different ways of getting there. The process share does just that. In this share, the outcome was the same for everyone: we wanted the kids to write for a longer time. However, the kids chose the specific strategy that would help them do that. In the end, everybody wrote for a longer time because each student could do so differently. If we had tried to force all the kids to use the same strategy, more than likely some kids would have been able to write for a longer time, while others wouldn't have been.

2. *They used their own language to explain complicated ideas.* You can probably imagine doing minilessons and conferences on

each of these topics, but there is no denying that a certain magic occurred as these four- and five-year-olds described their writing processes, using their young writing lives as examples. Where else but in a kindergarten process share would a student so honestly (and so accurately) announce that he needs a little rest before he digs in and writes some more? All too often we go somewhere outside of our students to help them with their writing process. How much simpler to remember that the biggest lessons can be found in the voices and examples of our students!

3. **They got to linger over ideas.** I began this share by asking, "How do we keep ourselves writing for a longer time?" April's students first thought about the question privately. This quiet time gave them each a chance to reflect on their own process. Then they got to discuss the question and hear what their friends thought. Hearing these different perspectives slowed down their thinking, and they were able to leave the conversation with many ways to increase their writing stamina.

Planning Tips: When Should You Conduct Process Shares?

A lively process conversation is great fun at any time, because it helps students of all ages create a writing process that's a good fit for them. However, there are certain times of the year that are particularly conducive to slowing your kids down and helping them reflect on and revise their writing process:

1. **When you want to build community or establish rituals and routines.** Often at the start of the year, there are many rituals and routines you must establish so that kids learn how to write independently. Process shares can help you do this. Whether you're talking about what to do when you don't know how to spell a word or how a partner can help you, the process share will get your kids actively involved in the creation of a writing community that is powerful

and can sustain itself. This type of work is essential at the start of the year, but it cannot stop there. In my favorite classrooms, teachers build a supportive and rigorous writing community by conducting process shares throughout the entire year. A process share is perfect whenever you have added some new rituals or routines. Perhaps you've asked your students to use a different-colored pen to make revisions or you've introduced observation notebooks as part of a poetry unit. You can conduct a process share in which you ask kids to reflect on how these new tools have affected their writing process.

2. *When you want to reinforce what was taught in the minilesson.* Process shares are great tools to use when you want to help your students gain a more thorough understanding of your minilesson. For example, if you presented a minilesson showing students how to play around with the order of their stories, you might want to conduct a process share that day in which several students talk about how they went about doing this.

3. *When you see confusion about or a lack of understanding of part of the writing process.* Observing your students, you may notice that some of them are confused by or unaware of parts of the writing process. In a second-grade classroom recently, I noticed that a significant number of students were chatting during writing workshop, having not yet experienced the rewards of a quiet writing time. I quickly pulled the class together and asked the children to write quietly for fifteen minutes. Afterward we discussed the experience. The kids marveled about how much more they accomplished in a quieter environment. They hadn't understood how much they needed that until they wrote quietly and had time to reflect on the experience.

Teaching Tips: Which Students Benefit Most from Process Shares?

Process shares are great for any kid at any time of the year, but you'll want to pay particular attention to *students who have difficulty with part of the writing process.* Perhaps you have students who have trou-

Don't Forget to Share: The Crucial Last Step in the Writing Workshop

ble getting started, who don't know what to do when they're finished, or who have trouble adding on. These kids will be more likely to follow through if they have taken a prominent role in a process share. I make sure I call on those students often and have them talk about what constitutes an exemplary writing process. (They can usually talk about it even if they're not yet doing it.) Afterward I'll give them complete credit for the idea and ask others to go to them if they're having trouble.

Additional Shares

You'll get tons of ideas for process shares by watching your students write. I created the following list by watching kids in hundreds of classrooms. Add your own ideas as you discover new ways to get your students talking about their processes.

Process Shares That Help Students Become More Independent

What did you do today when you didn't know how to spell a word?
What can you do if you don't know what to write about during writing workshop?
What kinds of problems did you encounter while writing today? How can we solve them together?
What can you do if you want to talk to the teacher but she's conferring with a student?

Process Shares That Help Students with Stamina

How did it feel to write for a long time?
What did you do to help yourself write for a longer time today?
How did it feel to write quietly?
What can we do to make sure that we always have some quiet time?

Process Shares That Help Students with Revision and Editing

Did anybody reread today while writing? How did that help you?
Some of you stayed with one piece of writing for a longer time. How did you do that?

How did rereading help you revise or edit your work?

What kinds of revision or editing did you find yourself doing today?

Process Shares That Help Students Work with a Partner

What was it like to work with a partner?

How did you and your partner help each other?

Did you and your partner have any problems? How did you solve them?

Speaking about collaboration, Lynn K. Rhodes and Curt Dudley-Marling have said, "It is rare for teachers or parents to benefit from student's perspectives on their school struggles" (1996, 302). Process shares are a great opportunity not only for us to benefit from our students' perspectives but also for our students to realize the insight and power they have to create optimal learning conditions for themselves and their classmates.

Process Shares at a Glance

What is a process share?	In a process share, the teacher poses a question that pertains to the writing process: *What do you do when you don't know how to spell a word? What do you do when you don't know what to write about?* The kids may or may not bring their writing with them, depending on what they will be talking about. Then the kids explore the question, using all of their prior writing experiences to help them.
When should you conduct process shares?	• When you want to build community or establish rituals and routines • When you want to reinforce what was taught in the minilesson • When you see confusion about or a lack of understanding of part of the writing process
Which students benefit most from process shares?	Students who have difficulty with part of the writing process

Progress Shares

Excellent job, Taras!
Is my teacher talking to me? Could this be true?
I actually did . . . good?
It couldn't be helped. I was scarred for life.
From then on writing was a significant part of my life.

—Taras Holoman

Recently I received the above as part of an email from Taras, whom I had taught in first grade. He remembered that I had celebrated his progress in front of the class and told me that my doing so had turned him on to writing. Interestingly, Taras "forgot" that we had argued constantly that year, that his eyes bugged out every time I attempted to hold him accountable for doing his best work. He missed more recesses than any other kid in my class, and when he did, he acted as if he couldn't care less. He forgot these moments—I think—because celebrating his progress made all the hard times worth it.

Taras' note reminded me of the power of celebration. But as important as I think celebration is, I still want to consider this question: How do we celebrate our students' progress in a way that benefits everyone? The answer lies in conducting shares in which students don't just honor one another's writing progress but also use these successes as ways to set goals for themselves.

What Is a Progress Share?

A progress share unfolds in one of two ways. Sometimes the conversation is focused around everybody's progress; sometimes it's focused on just one person's progress. In a progress share centered on everybody's progress, the teacher poses a question such as, "How has your writing improved in this unit of study?" The kids may or may not bring their writing with them, depending on what they will be talking about. The students then discuss the question and set goals for their future writing. In a progress share focused on one person's progress, that student shares her progress (and perhaps her writing) with the class. Afterward, the class uses that student's breakthrough as a springboard for discussing their own writing goals.

A Progress Share in Action

It's October in Camille Klingele's first-grade classroom; Camille is in the middle of a Small Moment unit of study.

Getting Ready

- The writing of the student who is sharing
- Touchstone texts and revision and editing correction tape are on hand but are not used on this particular day

Observations Before the Share

As Camille watches her kids, she notices Bill writing furiously; he is clearly using his time wisely and has produced several pages of text. Since Bill typically doesn't get much work done during writing workshop, a fact both he and the rest of the class are well aware of, Camille sees an opportunity to change not only the kids' perception of Bill but also Bill's perception of himself. She decides to conduct a progress share, after privately getting Bill to agree to talk about his progress and read his piece aloud.

Don't Forget to Share: The Crucial Last Step in the Writing Workshop

One of Camille's goals is for all her students to write a lot every day. She knows they can reach that goal if they can write without distraction. She addressed this in September; some of her students caught on, but others still have not. When she sees Bill writing a lot, she realizes it is the perfect opportunity not only to celebrate Bill but also to help many more kids use their writing time more wisely.

Setup

Camille: Today we're going to talk about Bill's progress. He wrote the entire time, and because of that he got a lot accomplished. We'll listen to Bill talk about his progress, and then afterward he'll read his story. We'll let him know all the smart things we think he's done. Finally, you'll get a chance to talk about which of those things you think you could also do.

First, Camille asks the kids to give Bill some compliments. This will help the class and Bill recognize the progress he has made. Because she wants to make sure that everyone benefits, she also lets the kids know that afterward they will set some goals for themselves.

Discussion

Bill: Today when Mrs. Klingele said that it was time to write, I got my paper, went to my quiet space, and just started working. Nobody bothered me, and look at how many pages I wrote in just one day. (*With great gusto, Bill holds up five pages that are stapled together into a book. He then reads his piece. Students laugh at the funny parts.*)

Students like Bill are often overlooked in a progress share, because it can be hard to see their progress. This is all the more reason to be vigilant in our observations. Camille has been watching Bill regularly and asked him to share the moment she saw progress.

Caleb: I want to hear the whole story again. It was funny!
Camille: I agree. It was funny. Bill, do you mind reading it again?
Bill: No. (*He does so eagerly.*)

Bill has never written anything this funny or this long, and it has been well received. It is a great moment not only for Bill but also for the rest of the kids. They have pigeonholed Bill as a student who never gets his work done, and he has shown them a different side of himself.

Camille: Let's take a quiet moment to think about the smart things that Bill has done. Once you have a compliment for him, put your eyes on Bill so he knows you're ready.

The students close their eyes and take a quiet moment to think.

Camille: Ally, do you want to share your compliment?

Ally: Your book is long and it is really, really funny!

Camille: Bill, I'm wondering, how did you write so much in one day?

Bill: I had a quiet space, and nobody bothered me there.

Camille: I know what you mean about a quiet space. I do my best writing when I'm in the library and nobody can distract me. Bill, do you think this is true about you? Are you the kind of writer who also needs a quiet space when you write?

Bill: Yes.

Camille: Then I'm going to make sure that you get that for the rest of the year. Some people don't need it to be completely quiet. Little noises and having people working around them aren't distracting.

Charlie: I'm that kind of writer. I don't mind noise. I just keep writing.

Camille: You're right, Charlie. I have noticed that about you. I want everybody to think about this question: What kind of writer are you? Are you like Bill and need your own space? Or are you like Charlie and little noises and other kids don't bother you? Please discuss this with a partner. (*The students turn and talk to the person next to them.*)

Camille artfully uses Bill's progress as a way to get the rest of the students to reflect on their own needs as writers. She has them do this in partnerships because she wants everyone to participate.

Camille: Hands up if you're like Bill, and you get distracted and need your own quiet space. (*About half the students put up a hand.*) That is important for me to know. I'm going to write your names down, because I'll change some of your writing spots so that you do have a quiet space. Hands up if you're like Charlie, and noise and people don't distract you. (*The other half of the kids put up a hand, and Camille writes their names down as well.*)

It's rare that students get an opportunity to reflect on their progress and set future goals. They need more of this—it's vital to their becoming life-long writers. Teachers sometimes question whether kids can take on this type of reflective stance. We have just seen that they can. Camille's students think about their needs as writers, and then Camille uses what they have said to make some changes in the classroom environment. Afterward, Camille and I look at the lists she has made. Most of the kids have been dead on in their self-analysis. She'll place the more distractible kids in quiet nooks and leave the others where they are. She'll also speak individually with the few students who she feels haven't accurately understood their need for quiet or their imperviousness to noise.

Camille: Writing a lot every day is a good goal, not just for Bill but for all of us. Bill has helped us understand that we'll reach that goal if we have good writing spots. Bill, you're now our class expert on getting down to business and getting a lot done during writing workshop. If anybody continues to have trouble with this, can he or she come and talk to you?

Bill: Yes.

Camille reinforces Bill's progress by asking him to help others. This is a great incentive and will help him to continue writing a lot in the future.

Future Teaching Ideas

- Writers have special writing spots that help them write a lot every day.
- Writers notice if other people are distracting to them. If so, they ask for a quiet space.
- Writers help themselves write a lot by doing the best they can when they get to hard parts.

The Special Power of Conversation

All of us have a few Bills in our class, and it's heartening to know that progress shares can instantly change their classroom status. Slowing down and having a conversation about Bill's progress had huge implications, not just for Bill but for all the students:

1. ***They made important instructional decisions.*** Camille asked Bill if he was the kind of writer that needed a quiet space, and he said yes. This was a crucial moment. Camille had conferred with

him about this many times, and he had been resistant to the idea of having a quiet spot to work. He wanted to be where the action was! When Camille insisted that he move to a quiet space, he was not at all happy about it. What a difference it made for Bill to try out having a quiet space and then decide himself that it was exactly what he needed. The rest of the kids made some decisions as well. They had to decide whether or not they were the kind of writer who needed a quiet space. Camille knew her students well and could have determined this on her own. She was tempted to skip this part of the conversation and just take over: "Sarah, you get distracted. You'll sit in a quiet nook!" But getting students to realize this for themselves goes a long way.

2. *They used their own language to explain complicated ideas.* In this progress share, Bill got to hear the other students say nice things about his writing. The words that students say to one another often have a far greater impact than the words we say to them. There's a good chance that Bill will continue writing a lot because he'll remember how much his friends enjoyed his story.

3. *They got to linger over ideas.* I'm embarrassed to admit how many times kids have achieved significant progress in my presence and all I've done is acknowledge it perfunctorily. If Camille had done that with Bill, he may not have followed through as readily. Camille slowed down his success so that everyone could savor it. She asked him to read his story once and then, based on the kids' reactions, urged him to read it again. Then she had the rest of the students think about what they needed in order to progress. She even made Bill the class expert, asking him to help others write more on subsequent days. All of this great conversation happened because of Bill's breakthrough!

A Close-in Look at Writing

To help us think about the impact that progress shares have on student writing, let's first look more closely at Bill. I spoke with Camille a few weeks after the share, and she told me that although Bill hadn't

Don't Forget to Share: The Crucial Last Step in the Writing Workshop

suddenly become the perfect student, he was using his writing time more wisely and writing more detailed pieces. Camille felt (and I agreed) that the progress share had been his invitation to become a different kind of student.

Let's also look at Skyasia, a first grader in Millie DeStefano's classroom. Skyasia was hesitant to write any words during writing workshop because she didn't want to take a risk. She also had limited understanding of letter-sound correspondence. One day I helped her add the word *me* next to a drawing of herself in her "story." Then I asked her to share that accomplishment with the class. When she did, she announced that this was the first time she had ever written words. She then asked her classmates to read her story and tell her which person she was. They were able to do this easily, and Skyasia was thrilled that they could read what she had written. From that day on she wrote words during writing workshop. I'm convinced it was because we had slowed down and reveled in her progress.

Planning Tips: When Should You Conduct Progress Shares?

Progress shares are a great way to boost morale and ensure a positive classroom community, so you'll want to conduct them all year, September through June. But there are some key times in the year when they're especially productive:

1. ***At the end of a unit of study.*** Many of you already celebrate students at the end of a unit. Now you can be more deliberate about not only celebrating them but also discussing their progress and setting new goals. There are several ways to do this. Some teachers have kids read their pieces aloud in small groups or in pairs and then have them discuss their progress with one another. Other teachers conduct what the Teachers College Reading and Writing Project calls a *museum share*. In a museum share, students lay their pieces out around the room, and other students (and perhaps teachers and parents) walk around and admire what everyone has

written. Many teachers also have children attach a comment sheet to their writing so that others can write down what they liked about it. You'll want each kid to stay close to his writing, answering any questions and of course reveling in all the compliments. Another way to get students talking about their progress is to have them choose their favorite word, sentence, or phrase from their writing and then read it into the quiet of the share circle. Afterward, the students could talk about the ways in which the class' writing has improved during the unit of study.

2. ***When breakthroughs occur.*** I tell teachers that they shouldn't wait for a student to make a breakthrough; they should make sure that every student has breakthroughs and has them regularly. Of course their next question is how to do that. We can help all our students make breakthroughs by being strict and kind at the same time. At the beginning of this chapter I told you about Taras, my former first-grade student, and some of the trying times we had. I was strict with him, and I continue to be strict with all the kids I work with. Ralph Fletcher, in his book *What a Writer Needs*, says, "A mentor builds on strength, often seeing more in a student's work than the student sees" (1993, 15). This is exactly why I am strict. I see more in my students than they see in themselves, and because of that I push them. That does not mean I am not kind. I am. As their mentor, I want them to see what I already know. And when they do make a breakthrough I drop everything and celebrate.

Teaching Tips: Which Students Benefit Most from Progress Shares?

There will be very few students who won't want to take part in a progress share. Who doesn't love a good celebration? But you'll want to think about which students in your class can especially use this boost and focus on them:

1. ***The English language learners.*** English language learners need plenty of practice speaking English in risk-free environments.

Don't Forget to Share: The Crucial Last Step in the Writing Workshop

Progress shares are a great opportunity for them to practice and celebrate their English. If in a conference a student speaks in a more detailed way than she normally does, I'll ask her if she will share her story orally. If she seems reluctant, I might say, "How about I share the start of your story and then you continue telling the rest?" or "How about I share your story first and then you share it a second time afterward?"

2. **Students who are capable of trying out what you have taught in a minilesson or conference but don't.** Some students resist minilesson instruction. At times, I confer with these kids and get them to try what I've taught in the minilesson. Once they do, I feature them in a progress share. This increases the likelihood that they'll follow through on my instruction in the future.

Additional Shares

There are so many ways for kids to talk about their progress and to set goals for themselves. You'll discover many of them by watching your students and seeing what they need in order to progress. Following are some possible topics for progress shares. You'll add lots more as you learn more about your students.

Progress Shares That Are Focused on One Student

Let's celebrate that you have written words that you know.
Let's celebrate that others can read your writing.
Let's celebrate that you wrote the entire time.
Let's celebrate that you tried a new writing topic.
Let's celebrate that you got started independently.
Let's celebrate that you told a story rich with details.
Let's celebrate that you reread and revised or edited your writing independently.
Let's celebrate that you stuck with one writing piece for a few days.
Let's celebrate that you wrote the words the best that you could.

Progress Shares That Are Focused on All Students

How has your writing improved during the nonfiction unit of study?
In what ways do you work more independently now than you did
    at the start of the year?
How has your writer's notebook changed over the last few months?
Are you using it in wiser ways?

John Dewey says, "To be education a learning experience must not
only generate fact knowledge or belief, it must also increase the likelihood that the learner will actually seek similar experiences in the future"
(1938). When we celebrate progress in our shares we are creating pleas-
urable experiences for our kids that make it more likely they'll seek similar experiences in the future. Isn't that what great education is all about?

Progress Shares at a Glance

What is a progress share?	A progress share unfolds in one of two ways. Sometimes the conversation is focused around everybody's progress; sometimes it's focused on just one person's progress. In a progress share centered on everybody's progress, the teacher poses a question such as, *How has your writing improved in this unit of study?* The kids may or may not bring their writing with them, depending on what they will be talking about. The students then discuss the question and set goals for their future writing. In a progress share focused on one person's progress, that student shares her progress (and perhaps her writing) with the class. Afterward, the classmates use that student's breakthrough as a springboard for discussing their own writing goals.
When should you conduct progress shares?	• At the end of a unit of study • When breakthroughs occur
Which students benefit most from progress shares?	• English language learners • Students who are capable of trying out what you have taught in a minilesson or conference but don't

---

Don't Forget to Share: The Crucial Last Step in the Writing Workshop

Partner and Small-Group Shares

In a two-person dialogue there is far more opportunity for
both speakers to engage in a piece of connected discourse,
to alternately take the roles of speaker and listener and to use
language to challenge and clarify thinking.

—Pauline Gibbons, *Learning to Learn in a Second Language*

It's Wednesday afternoon in Shawn Brandon's first-grade classroom
at PS 11, and Alexis and Corey are sitting hip-to-hip with their writing between them. I watch the two of them reading Corey's story;
when they finish, they read Alexis'. During each reading, they point to
particular places in the text and make comments. At one point Alexis
says, "That word doesn't look right, and I think it's on our word wall.
Let's go check." They run up full speed to check the word and then
return to finish editing their writing together. Across town, in Ellen
McCrum's fifth-grade classroom at PS 234, small groups of students are
dispersed throughout the room. As Ellen moves among the groups, she
hears students reading their memoir pieces aloud, noticing one
another's craft, and then making plans for new craft techniques they'll
try tomorrow. Shawn's and Ellen's kids, although in two different
grades, are all reaping the benefits of having writing conversations in a
more intimate setting.

Up till now I've been describing shares involving the entire class.
These types of shares are very much needed, but they have their limi-
tations. Real writers usually prefer to talk about their writing with one
other person, or perhaps with a small group. Partner and small-group
shares can help bring the real world of writing into your classroom.

What Is a Partner Share?

In a partner share, two students talk about their writing. These conversations are very similar to those that take place during whole-group share sessions, with one exception: now their ideas are shared with just one other person. An additional benefit of a partner share is that because kids can see each other's writing more easily, they can also help each other with editing.

One of the first things you'll have to decide when launching writing partnerships is how to match up students. Some teachers make these decisions on their own; others ask the kids for input. Either way, you'll want to pair students who are at similar skill levels, so that both students benefit from the collaboration. You'll also need to keep your students' personalities in mind, matching students who you think will be compatible.

A Partner Share in Action

In Shawn Brandon's first-grade classroom, Gwen and Bella are in the middle of their collaboration. Previously they've discussed who will read her writing aloud first. Bella has deferred to Gwen but has asked if she can go first next time. Gwen has agreed and then read her story, which is about a boy and a girl and their short-lived love affair. (See Figure 7.1 on pages 81–84).

Gwen: I don't know what I should say on the last page. I don't know how I should end it.

Bella: I'm wondering how come the boy had to leave the girl?

Gwen: He was in love with the girl, but he didn't know what to say to her, so he just left. He never got to say "I love you."

Bella (*laughing*): How did the boy feel when he left?

Gwen: He was sad.

Bella: It's up to you because you're the writer, but maybe on the last page you could just say, "The boy was sad."

Gwen: That's a great idea. (*She quickly writes, "The boy went home sad."*)

Don't Forget to Share: The Crucial Last Step in the Writing Workshop

Figure 7.1   Gwen's Piece

The Boy and the girl.

by Gwendolyn Lee

Bella: I want to write a story about a very mean frog who acts like a bully all of the time.

Gwen: Hey, your book is going to have a frog in it, just like *Frog and Toad*!

Bella: I know. I have a *Frog and Toad* book with me. (*She holds it up.*)

Gwen: I have an idea. Maybe you could have chapters just like the *Frog and Toad* books do. You see how this book has a table of contents, and then there are little stories about Frog and Toad? Maybe you could have some little stories about your frog and how mean he is.

Bella: That's a great idea. Chapter 1 could be called "At the Playground." Chapter 2 could be called "At Writing Workshop." Chapter 3 could be called "Someone Getting Hurt." In this chapter the mean frog is going to hurt someone and then lose all of his friends.

Figure 7.1   Continued

Ouac upan
a taim
tair was
a boy woh
was inlove
with a girl...

The boy
did not
korr wait
he writ
to say.

Don't Forget to Share: The Crucial Last Step in the Writing Workshop

Figure 7.1   Continued

finlee The boy got to meet the girl.

Figure 7.1 Continued

The Special Power of Partner Conversation

Partner shares are a vital learning tool. Many people shy away from partner shares, perhaps because they are harder to manage. Kids are scattered around the room, rather than assembled in a close-knit circle. Although we try to give students some direction in how to share with each other, each partnership is sure to go a bit differently, and we can't work with fifteen partnerships at once. All that said, I believe what kids get from working with a partner is worth the slightly out-of-control feeling we may sometimes have. Here are some benefits that kids receive from working in pairs:

1. ***They have opportunities to do things independently.*** Many times in whole-group shares, we'll see kids do something for the first time and afterward breathe a sigh of relief: *Phew, they got it! They're all set now.* While it's true that those kids are on the right track, we have to remember that they achieved this success underneath their teacher's watchful eye; the process has probably not yet been internalized. Partner shares give kids opportunities to practice things by themselves so that they can internalize them. Gwen and Bella used a lot of the language Shawn had introduced in the whole-group share. I wasn't surprised to hear Gwen specifically ask Bella for help with her ending, because Shawn often told the kids in whole-class shares that they should let each other know the exact type of help that they wanted. Later in the conversation, Bella said, "I'm wondering," and, "It's up to you because you're the writer." She had heard and used these phrases over and over again in whole-group shares and now had a chance to try them on her own. It was also neat to hear Gwen suggest that Bella include different chapters in her frog book like the ones in Arnold Lobel's *Frog and Toad* books. Both Gwen and Bella had been a part of many craft shares that year in which touchstone texts had been introduced into the conversation, and the partnership structure gave them a chance to try this themselves.

2. ***Quieter voices are brought out.*** It can be intimidating for our shy students to share their ideas in large groups. Many of those kids find it easier to share in a more intimate setting, such as a partnership. Bella, for example, always listened in the whole-group shares but almost never contributed. It was exciting to watch her come out of her shell in her partnership with Gwen.

3. ***They have an eager audience for their writing.*** In many whole-group shares only a few students read their writing aloud; there are even times when nobody does. Looking at fewer pieces of writing helps keep the conversation focused, but it doesn't allow kids to have a consistent audience. Mem Fox, in a keynote speech at Columbia University, said that it is the "reader that makes the writing matter." That makes a lot of sense. When I write for publication, I have my audience in mind, and I make my best revisions after thinking about what my readers need in order to understand what I'm trying to say. Because I'm an adult and an experienced writer, I don't always need to see my readers. I know they are there.

Partner shares are just one of many ways to give our students a concrete and consistent audience.

4. ***There is more accountability.*** No matter how much we try to hold students accountable for participating in whole-class shares, we know that on some days some students will daydream or choose not to participate. Despite our best efforts, it's hard to keep everyone engaged. In partner shares, it's tougher to fade into the background; each student has a great deal more responsibility in keeping the conversation going.

What Is a Small-Group Share?

In a small-group share, several students (usually between three and six) come together for a conversation. Small-group shares are usually introduced after kids have become comfortable working in pairs. Although they may not be appropriate for our youngest writers, some teachers pull these shares off just fine at that age level. For the most part, I keep younger students (grades K–2) in partner shares for the entire year and move older kids (grades 3–5) into small-group shares only after I know they can work successfully with a partner.

A Small-Group Share in Action

Ellen McCrum's fifth graders are working in small groups to revise their outlines for their research reports. One group is made up of three boys, Nick, John, and James.

Nick: My main topic is the Lenape Indians and how they lived their lives. My subtopics are family, government, religion, culture, and their interaction with the Dutch.

John: I don't think that you need to talk about the government, because it doesn't seem to fit in with how they lived their lives.

Nick: I was thinking I could say something about how their government worked, like whether it was a democracy or a monarchy. And

Don't Forget to Share: The Crucial Last Step in the Writing Workshop

then after that I would explain how the type of government they had affected their lives.

John: OK, I guess that fits in, but what about the Dutch?

Nick: I want to teach my readers about how the Dutch took the land from the Lenape Indians unfairly.

John: Well, I don't think it fits in, if you want to teach people about the way they lived their lives.

Nick: Well, maybe I could end with that part. I could talk about how their lives changed when the Dutch came and took their land.

John: OK. My main topic is Thomas Edison. My subtopics are his first invention, the lightbulb, and how he changed the world through his inventions.

Nick: Could you include something about his childhood to bring the reader into the story?

John: Yeah, I want to put that into the first paragraph. I read in a book that he had his first science lab when he was ten, and that he wasn't good in school at all.

Nick: Like Albert Einstein.

James: I think your outline is fine the way it is. My topic is Bill Gates and how he changed the world of computers. My subtopics are Would computers be the same without Bill Gates? What did he create? How did he crush the competition? Why did he start a charity? How did his success with computers help him become a philanthropist? Why is he important?

Nick: I think you could add some facts about how Bill Gates is the richest person in the world.

John: I don't get why you would talk about the charity if your purpose was to teach about how Bill Gates changed the computer world.

Nick: Maybe you could change the purpose of your piece and show Bill Gates has changed the entire world, not just the computer world. Then everything fits in. (Figure 7.2 is John's draft of his article on Thomas Edison based on the feedback he received in his small group.)

Figure 7.2   Draft of John's Thomas Edison Piece

John Z
March 28, 2006

THOMAS ALVA EDISON

"Results? Why, man, I have gotten lots of results! If I find 10,000 ways something won't work, I haven't failed. I am not discouraged, because every wrong attempt discarded is often a step forward..."

The light bulb, etheric force, the phonograph, the stock ticker, motion-picture camera and x-rays. Without them the world would not have light that fills a whole room, or light to push out the dark. The discovery of *"Etheric Force"*. Without it we would not have radios. Edison's invention creates the "Edison Effect" which inspires the science of electronics. Thomas Alva Edison was the inventor of amazing things and through his inventions, he changed the world.

Thomas was born on February 11, 1847 in Milan, Ohio the son of Nancy and Samuel Edison. Thomas was the youngest in his family and had 6 siblings. Thomas moved when he was 7 and in his new school he always got the worst grades. His mother heard the teacher say that Thomas was "addled", so she took him and taught him at home. Thomas Edison did not like doing his chores or going to school. He thought that he could do whatever he wanted to do. At ten Thomas has a little laboratory and he did experiments all day.

From 1864-1867 Thomas worked as a tramp telegrapher in states from Michigan to Louisiana. When he was in his 20's, he went to New York and invented the stock ticker. In 1871 Thomas married Mary Stairwell. In 1877 he invented the phonograph and people were amazed. In 1879 he invents the light bulb and gives a demonstration at Menlo Park. In 1882 he invents the first power and lightning station (in London, England).

Without electricity we would only have candles to walk around with but with electricity we flick a button and we get light from a light bulb. Without Thomas Edison discovering the "Electric Force", Marconi would not have invented the radio. Also he invented the practical fluoroscope which helped surgeons perform the first x-ray. Eventually after Edison left home, he set up a laboratory in Menlo Park, NJ where he got the idea of inventing the light bulb, phonograph, telegraph and telephone, He also had memorials at Menlo park. After he got the ideas for inventions he would sometimes try them at Menlo Park.

Edisons life ended 2 years after the fifteenth anniversary of the light bulb. He died on October 18 at his home in West Orange, New Jersey at the age of 84. In his lifetime he invented more than 20 inventions and helped others to invent and become famous. Edison was not just an inventor he was head of the Navel Consulting Board, and he worked on inventions to help the US Navy in World War I.

Bibliography
Buranelli, Vincent. Thomas Alva Edison. Englewood Cliffs: Silver Burdett Press, 1989.
Guthridge, Sue. Thomas A. Edison Young Inventor. New York: Simon & Schuster, 1947.

The Special Power of Small-Group Conversations

Small-group shares take conversations to a new level. John, Nick, and James benefited from their small group in many of the same ways that Bella and Gwen did from their partnership, but they had some additional benefits and responsibilities:

1. ***They had opportunities to do things independently.*** The kids in this group had already tried out all these conversational moves in whole-group shares. Now they had to use them on their own, listening carefully to one another and speaking up when they disagreed. John, for example, told Nick that he should take out the subtopic of government because it didn't fit in with his big idea of how the Lenape Indians lived their lives. Nick disagreed, and John listened to what Nick had to say and revised his feedback. Later, when speaking about James' outline, Nick and John tried to help him rework his purpose so that he could include the facts about Bill Gate's charities.

2. ***They got to hear more than one perspective.*** Each student in the group got specific feedback on his outline from more than one person. Sometimes the feedback was the same, sometimes it was different, which is exactly what happens when you show your writing to more than one person. These multiple perspectives gave the students more insight into their writing, within the important context of listening to what everyone said and choosing which advice to take based on what they thought would improve their writing.

A Continuum of Partner and Small-Group Shares

At this point, you may be wondering, *How would these partner and small-group shares go in my classroom? Would I tell my kids what to do each day, or would they decide for themselves?* These are great questions. The truth is, these shares will look different in different grades, in different classrooms, and at different times of the year. To help you see all the possibilities, I've developed a continuum of how partner and small-group shares might evolve in your classroom. It starts with a considerable amount of teacher direction and ends with students making most of the decisions on their own. Use this continuum in whatever way you like. You might follow the path of progressive independence that is indicated here or pick and choose approaches that feel most relevant in given situations.

1. *All partnerships are doing the same thing.* The easiest way to begin is to tell students exactly what they'll talk about in their partnerships: "Today I want you and your partner to help each other revise your writing," or "Today I want you to talk to your partner about how rereading helps you edit your work." Giving your students specific instructions for each share makes it easier for them eventually to choose what they'll do on their own. After you've given specific instructions for a while, you can confer with a few partnerships, showing them how to make these decisions themselves. Those students could then share with the whole group as a way to get the rest of the kids ready for what's coming.

2. *Each partnership is doing something different.* Once students have practiced the different types of shares, you'll be able to let go of the reins and prompt them to decide for themselves what type of share they want to do: "Writers, you know that you and your partner can do content shares, craft shares, process shares, and progress shares. Today and every day, you can make this decision by yourselves. You and your partner can talk together and think about the kind of help you need." A chart like the one in Figure 7.3 can help kids make these decisions.

3. *All the small groups are doing the same thing.* When upper-grade (grades 3–5) students become comfortable in partnerships, you'll want to show them how to do similar work in small groups. The easiest way, at least in the beginning, is to give students some direction on what to talk about. For example, Ellen McCrum divided her students into small groups and asked them to help one another revise their research report outlines.

4. *Each small group is doing something different.* After a bit of practice, the kids will be more than ready to choose what they'll talk about in their small groups. At this point, you'll need to reconsider how small groups will be formed. Some teachers form groups based

IF . . .	THEN . . .
We need revision help.	We should do a content share.
We need craft help.	We should do a craft share.
We need to expand our writing process.	We should do a process share.
We want to celebrate what we've accomplished.	We should do a progress share.

on what writers want to talk about. For example, the five kids who want to talk about new craft ideas might make up one group, and another group might consist of kids who want to talk about an aspect of their writing process. Other teachers assign groups based on personalities, and once the group is formed the kids decide what they'll talk about. Either way, kids assess their needs and choose what to do based on those needs. The chart in Figure 7.3 is helpful here as well.

5. ***Small groups work together for an extended period.*** This is just a matter of duration. Rather than meeting together once and then disbanding, the groups remain together for a number of days or weeks as they work on an ongoing project.

Units of Study Devoted to Partner and Small-Group Shares

A number of teachers who read drafts of this chapter remarked that partner and small-group shares sounded wonderful but that they could never quite get them to work in their classrooms. The reason could be that we don't give kids enough instruction on how the shares should go. Figure 7.4 outlines a four-week unit of study on partner shares, and Figure 7.5 outlines a four-week unit of study on small-group shares.

Getting Ready

- Form partnerships: decide if you will enlist the students in helping you or if you'll form the pairs or partners on your own.

Week 1: What Do Partnerships Look and Sound Like?

- Partners sit hip-to-hip while reading each other's writing.
- Partners sit knee-to-knee when talking about each other's writing.
- Partners decide who will share first.
- Partners listen carefully to each other, making sure that they understand and that they speak up when they don't.
- Partners use much of the language that has already been practiced in whole-group shares. (Brainstorm speaking and listening prompts. See Figure 7.6.)

Weeks 2 and 3: Partners Can Have Many Types of Conversations

- Partners can have content conversations.
- What are some possible things that we can say to one another in a content share? (Brainstorm content share prompts. See Figure 7.7.)
- Partners can have craft conversations.
- What are some possible things that we can say to one another in a craft share? (Brainstorm craft share prompts. See Figure 7.8.)
- Partners can have process conversations.
- What are some possible things we can say to one another in a process share? (Brainstorm process share prompts. See Figure 7.9.)
- Partners can have progress conversations.
- What are some possible things we can say to one another in a progress share? (Brainstorm progress share prompts. See Figure 7.10.)
- Partners can have editing conversations.
- What are some possible things we can say to one another in an editing share? (Brainstorm editing share prompts. See Figure 7.11.)

Week 4: Partners Can Choose Different Types of Conversations to Have

- Partners decide the type of help they need and then they choose the type of share they'll do.
- Partners take turns choosing the types of share they'll do.

OR

- Partners do more than one thing in their share meeting.

Getting Ready

- Form small groups: decide whether you will form these groups or enlist the help of your students.

Week 1: What Do Small Groups Look and Sound Like?

- Small groups should sit in a circle with their writing in front of them. Only the student sharing has his piece of writing in his lap.
- The group must decide who will share first.
- Group members must speak up when they can't hear someone.
- Members can use the language they've learned in whole-class and partner shares to help them communicate.

Week 2: Small Groups Can Have Many Types of Conversations

- Small groups can discuss the content of one another's writing. (Give them a content prompt sheet to use if they run into trouble. See Figure 7.7.)
- Small groups can discuss the craft of one another's writing. (Give them a craft prompt sheet to use if they run into trouble. See Figure 7.8.)
- Small groups can discuss their writing processes. (Give them a process prompt sheet to use if they run into trouble. See Figure 7.9.)
- Small groups can discuss their writing progress. (Give them a progress prompt sheet to use if they run into trouble. See Figure 7.10.)
- Small groups can help each other with editing. (Give them an editing prompt sheet to use if they run into trouble. See Figure 7.11.)

Week 3: Small Groups Choose What to Talk About

- Decide how groups will be formed. Will they be formed based on interest?
                                    OR
  Will they be formed based on skills and personalities? If this is the case, the group members will have to negotiate what they'll talk about.
- Are there some members who are monopolizing the conversation? If so, how do we help bring out the quieter voices?
- How do we listen and respond to one another's questions and comments?
- How do we deal with differing opinions?

Figure 7.5   Continued

Week 4: Small Groups Can Make Long-Range Plans

- Small groups end their sessions by planning what they'll do in future share sessions. Will we do the same type of share next time or are we ready to try a new type of share?
- Small groups give one another writing homework. Members are responsible for following through.
- Small groups make sure that each member's needs are being met.

Figure 7.6   Speaking and Listening Prompts

When speaking to your partner or small-group members you might say:

- Could you speak up? I can't hear you.
- What does _____ mean?
- I agree with what you said because _____.
- I disagree with what you said because _____.

These units of study can be implemented in several ways. You can of course present one unit or both units in their entirety. This is best done closer to the second half of the year, so that kids have time to get comfortable with whole-class shares first. Alternatively, you can break up the units into shorter chunks. For example, you might work on logistics (weeks 1 and 2) early in the year and then introduce the more sophisticated work (weeks 3 and 4) later in the year.

However you decide to conduct these units of study, it's important to adjust them to fit the strengths and needs of your students. In addition, my guidelines for prompts in Figures 7.6–7.11 may need to be adjusted for your individual students and grade level. Here are some things you'll want to keep in mind:

1. *You don't need to wait until you conduct a unit of study to have kids work in partnerships or small groups.* Kids benefit tremendously from talking about their writing with others, and they

Figure 7.7   Content Share Prompts

In a content share you might say:

- I need help with my _____.
- Let me retell your piece to make sure I understand.
- Did I get it right?
- I was confused about the part when _____. Could you say more about that part?
- What does _____ mean?
- What's the most important part of your writing?
- What are you really trying to say in this piece of writing?
- Who is your audience? What else would your readers need to know in order to understand your writing?
- I think that your readers might want to know _____.
- I think that you should add what you just said into your writing.
- It's up to you because you are the writer, but I think you should add _____ because _____.
- Why do you think I should add that part?
- Why do you think I should take out that part?
- I agree with your suggestion because _____.
- I'm not sure I agree with your suggestion because _____.

Figure 7.8   Craft Share Prompts

In a craft share you might say:

- I tried _____ in my writing because _____.
- What I did in my writing is the same as _____ [a piece of literature or another student's writing].
- Here is what my writing would sound like if I tried _____.
- Let's reread our writing and imagine what it would sound like with these new craft ideas.
- There is a book that reminds me of what you've written. Let me show it to you.

Figure 7.9   Process Share Prompts

In a process share you might say:

- Which parts of your writing process are going well?
- Which parts of your writing process are not going well?
- How do you go about _____?
- How does rereading help you?
- What do you do when you don't know what to write about?

Figure 7.10   Progress Share Prompts

In a progress share you might say:

- I liked the way that you _____. I'm going to make that a goal for myself as well.
- A new goal I have is _____. I can achieve this goal by _____.
- I can help you achieve that goal by _____.
- How do you think you can continue the work that you started today?

should work in partnerships or small groups right from the start. Their collaboration won't be perfect, but you'll be watching what they are doing naturally and be able to teach to that later, in minilessons or a complete unit of study.

2. *You can conduct minilessons in the middle of writing workshop.* Typically, you teach a minilesson at the beginning of writing workshop, then your students work independently, and finally you end with a share. During a unit of study on partnerships or small groups, you might want to shift things a bit: begin by having students work on their own and then have them gather for a minilesson about an aspect of partnerships or small groups, after which students can join their partner or small group and immediately

Figure 7.11   Editing Share Prompts

In an editing share you might say:

- This part doesn't make sense. I think you should add

  _____.

- Let's reread to see if it makes sense now.
- This part of your writing doesn't quite sound right. You might say

  _____ instead of _____.

- Let's reread it to see if we think it sounds right now.
- I think you need to add a comma [or other punctuation mark] to help the reader.
- Let's reread to see if you need to add any punctuation to help the reader.
- That word doesn't look right to me. I think it is spelled

  _____. Let's look at the word together to see if we think it looks right now.

---

apply what they've learned. Even when you begin writing workshop with a minilesson, you can interject a midworkshop teaching point to remind the kids to apply what they have just learned.

3. ***Partner and small-group minilessons should include plenty of demonstration.*** A particularly effective means of demonstrating is the fishbowl. All this means is that a partnership or a small group has their conversation while the rest of the class watches and reflects on what is taking place. Choose a partnership or small group that you feel others will learn from. In addition, you the teacher can also take a role in the demonstration yourself. Sometimes I'll model a partner or small-group share in which everything goes smoothly; other times, I'll include problems and then demonstrate how I go about solving them.

4. ***Confer with partners and small groups about what they are doing.*** In Helen Yu's third-grade classroom recently, I was conferring with a small group of students who were revising their writing. When I asked them how the work was going, they proudly pulled out a tally sheet. Each of them had written three possible endings to his

or her story and then passed the endings around; everyone in the group voted on the ending he or she liked best. First I helped them have a discussion about what they liked about all the different endings. Then I reminded them that the best way to help one another revise was not through tally sheets but through conversations.

5. ***Charts or prompt sheets can be helpful.*** More than likely, your students will develop their own ways of speaking and listening to one another. But there will be some kids who need some additional support. Figures 7.6 through 7.11 list possible prompts you might teach your kids to use in both partner and small-group shares. Upper-grade teachers might create similar prompts with their students and then give each student a copy of the prompts; primary teachers might simply display these prompts on a classroom chart. Make sure kids understand that they don't have to use these prompts but that they're helpful when they don't know what to say. The prompts shouldn't be limiting; kids should feel free to talk to one another in ways that feel natural.

My hope is that the share sessions in your classroom will resemble the sharing you do in real life. Most important, I hope that inside each of your share meetings are "bits and pieces" of you and of your students. Let's make Leah Shenyer's vision of sharing a reality in classrooms around the world!

Don't Forget to Share: The Crucial Last Step in the Writing Workshop

Appendix A

Recommended Professional Literature on the Writing Workshop

Anderson, Carl. 2000. *How's It Going?* Portsmouth, NH: Heinemann.

Anderson, Carl. 2005. *Assessing Writers*. Portsmouth, NH: Heinemann.

Atwell, Nancie. 1998. *In the Middle: New Understandings About Writing, Reading, and Learning*. Portsmouth, NH: Heinemann.

Avery, Carol. 2002. . . . *And with a Light Touch*. 2d ed. Portsmouth, NH: Heinemann.

Calkins, Lucy, and colleagues from the Teachers College Reading and Writing Project. 2003. *Units of Study in Primary Writing: A Yearlong Curriculum*. Portsmouth, NH: Heinemann.

Calkins, Lucy, and collegues from the Teacher's College Reading and Writing Project. 2006. *Units of Study for Teaching Writing, Grades 3–5*. Portsmouth, NH: Heinemann.

Calkins, Lucy. 1994. *The Art of Teaching Writing*. Portsmouth, NH: Heinemann.

Clay, Marie. 1998. *Different Paths to Common Outcomes*. Portland, ME: Stenhouse.

Fletcher, Ralph, and JoAnn Portalupi. 2001. *The Writing Workshop: The Essential Guide*. Portsmouth NH: Heinemann.

Graves, Donald. 1983. *Writing: Teachers and Children at Work*. Portsmouth, NH: Heinemann.

Harwayne, Shelley. 2001. *Writing Through Childhood: Rethinking Process and Product*. Portsmouth, NH: Heinemann.

Hindley, Joanne. 1996. *In the Company of Children*. Portland, ME: Stenhouse.

Mermelstein, Leah. 2006. *Reading/Writing Connections in the K–2 Classroom: Find the Clarity and Then Blur the Lines*. Boston: Allyn and Bacon.

Wood Ray, Katie. 1999. *Wondrous Words: Writers and Writing in the Elementary Classroom*. Urbana, IL: National Council of Teacher of English.

Wood Ray, Katie, and Lisa Cleaveland. 2004. *About the Authors: Writing Workshop with Our Youngest Writers*. Portsmouth, NH: Heinemann.

Wood Ray, Katie, with Lester Laminack. 2001. *The Writing Workshop: Working Through the Hard Parts (and They're All Hard Parts)*. Urbana, IL: National Council of Teachers of English.

Appendix B

Teacher Checklist for Share Sessions

GETTING READY

_____Are you conducting share sessions every day?

_____Have you designated an area in the room where you and your students can gather?

_____Do your students know what materials to bring with them?

_____Do you have your own materials close by?

STUDENTS' ROLE

_____Do students listen to one another and speak up when they're confused?

_____Do students both give and get ideas?

_____Are students preparing for the share session? (Are they rereading their writing beforehand? Using think time to prepare their contributions?)

TEACHER'S ROLE

Are you using your observations to help you

_____plan for the types of shares that you'll conduct?

_____decide which kids will read their writing aloud?

_____set up the share sessions?

Are you observing your students during the shares to help you

_____give support when needed?

_____plan for future teaching?

_____Are your shares a positive experience for everyone? If not, how can you change this?

_____Are you teaching in direct response to what students say? Are you helping yourself do this by

    _____knowing your students?

    _____knowing your unit-of-study goals?

    _____keeping helpful materials nearby?

Are you teaching by

_____reinforcing?

_____providing more than one example?

_____demonstrating?

TYPES OF SHARES

_____Are you conducting content shares?

_____Are you conducting craft shares?

_____Are you conducting process shares?

_____Are you conducting progress shares?

_____Are you conducting partner shares?

_____Are you conducting small-group shares?

Appendix C

Touchstone Texts

Although I have separate book lists for both the upper and the lower grades, I'm sure many primary-grade teachers will find the upper-grade books helpful and vice versa.

Touchstone Texts for Writers in the Primary Grades

Launching the Writing Workshop

Fanelli, Sara. 1995. *My Map Book*. New York: Harper Collins.

Janeczka, Paul, comp. 1990. *The Place My Words Are Looking For*. New York: Simon and Schuster.

Story (Personal Narrative and Realistic Fiction)

Brinkloe, Julie. 1986. *Fireflies*. New York: Aladdin Paperbacks.

Crews, Donald. 1992. *Shortcut*. New York: Greenwillow.

Johnson, Angela. 1992. *The Leaving Morning*. New York: Orchard.

Keats, Ezra Jack. 1962. *The Snowy Day*. New York: Penguin Putnam Books for Young Readers.

Rylant, Cynthia. 1987–. The Henry and Mudge series. New York: Aladdin Paperbacks.

Willems, Mo. 2004. *Knuffle Bunny*. New York: Scholastic.

Writing for Many Reasons

Kroll, Steven. 2001. *Patches Lost and Found*. New York: Winslow.

Pak, Soyung. 1999. *Dear Juno*. New York: Puffin.

Nonfiction

Gibbons, Gail. 1999. *Pigs, Pigs, Pigs*. New York: Holiday House.

Jenkins, Steve. 2004. *Actual Size*. Boston: Houghton Mifflin.

Morris, Ann. 1992. *Houses and Homes*. New York: HarperCollins.

Moore, Helen, and Talas, Terry. 1996. *Beavers*. New York: Mondo.

Poetry

Greenfield, Eloise. 1972. *Honey, I Love*. New York: Harper Trophy.

Greenfield, Eloise. 1991. *Under the Sunday Tree*. New York: Harper Trophy.

Grimes, Nikki. 1997. *Meet Danitra Brown*. New York: Harper Trophy.

Touchstone Texts for Writers in the Upper Grades

Launching the Writing Workshop

Grimes, Nikki. 2000. *Jazmin's Notebook*. London: Puffin.

Story (Personal Narrative and Realistic Fiction)

Hesse, Karen. 1999. *Come on, Rain!* New York: Scholastic.

Munsch, Robert. 1993. *Wait and See.* Toronto, ON: Annick.

Ryder, Joanne. 1994. *My Father's Hands.* New York: Morrow Junior.

Rylant, Cynthia. 1985. *Every Living Thing.* New York: Aladdin Paperbacks.

Rylant, Cynthia. 1986. *Night in the Country.* New York: Aladdin Paperbacks.

Williams, Vera B. 1984. *A Chair for My Mother.* New York: Harper Trophy.

Memoir

Ehrlich, Amy, ed. 2001. *When I Was Your Age, Volume 1: Original Stories About Growing Up.* Cambridge, MA: Candlewick.

Woodson, Jacqueline. 2000. *Sweet Sweet Memory.* New York: Jump at the Sun.

Nonfiction

Kitchen, Bert. 1994. *Somewhere Today.* Cambridge, MA: Candlewick.

Stead, Tony, with Judy Ballester and Her Fourth-Grade Class. 2002. *Should There Be Zoos? A Persuasive Text.* New York: Mondo.

Wulffson, Don, and Laurie Keller. 2000. *Toys.* New York: Henry Holt.

Yolen, Jane. 1993. *Welcome to the Greenhouse.* New York: Putnam.

Poetry

Fletcher, Ralph. 1991. *Water Planet.* Paramus, NJ: Arrowhead.

Greenfield, Eloise. 1988. *Under the Sunday Tree.* New York: Harper Trophy.

Heard, Georgia. 1997. *Creatures of Earth, Sea, and Sky.* Honesdale, PA: Boyds Mills.

Appendix D

A Possible Recordkeeping System for Share Sessions

Week of: _____

Unit of study: _____

Days of week		What type of share session did I conduct?		
Monday: _____		1. Content share		
Tuesday: _____		2. Craft share		
Wednesday: _____		3. Process share		
Thursday: _____		4. Progress share		
Friday: _____		5. Partner share		
		6. Small-group share		
Dante	Courtney	Bridget	Sal	Skyasia
Ricky	Yasmine	Jonas	Pedro	Robert
Claire	Fantasia	Yashira	Thomas	Raul
Paul	Katelyn	Ricky	Lori	Tanya
Scott	Jose	Vicky		

Legend

R: Student read his or her writing aloud.

L: Student was actively listening.

C: Student contributed an idea.

Notes (future minilessons, conferences, or share sessions)

A Month of Share Sessions in Millie DeStefano's First-Grade Classroom

Time of year: October

Unit of study: Small Moments (Focused Narrative)

Day 1:
Craft
  Share
	Day 2:
	Craft
	  Share
		Day 3:
		Craft
		  Share
			Day 4:
			Craft
			  Share
				Day 5:
				Process Share
				(How do you find ideas for your small moments?)

Day 6:
Content
  Share
	Day 7:
	Content
	  Share
		Day 8:
		Content
		  Share
			Day 9:
			Progress
			  Share
				Day 10:
				Partner
				  Share

Day 11:
Content
  Share
	Day 12:
	Content
	  Share
		Day 13:
		Content
		  Share
			Day 14:
			Content
			  Share
				Day 15:
				Partner
				  Share

Day 16:
Partner
  Share
	Day 17:
	Partner
	  Share
		Day 18:
		Partner
		  Share
			Day 19:
			Progress
			  Share
				Day 20:
				Process
				  Share

Millie's unit of study began with immersion (days 1–4). She expanded upon the immersion by having her students also talk about craft during the share sessions. When students began writing on day 5, Millie noticed that some students were having trouble coming up with topic ideas. She decided to address this issue in a process share. On days 6–8 she conducted content shares to prepare students for the upcoming revision minilessons. On day 9 the class celebrated some of their accomplishments; on day 10 the students did this same work in partnerships. The following week (days 11–14) Millie continued to work with the students on revision through content shares. On day 15 they did similar work with partners. On the last week (days 16–18) of the study, the students, in pairs, helped each other revise and edit their writing. They celebrated their final pieces on day 19 and made goals for their future work. Millie conducted a process share on day 20 during which the students talked about the ways that rereading helped them revise and edit their work.

Appendix F

A Month of Share Sessions in Ellen McCrum's Fifth-Grade Classroom

Time of year: March

Unit of study: Informational Nonfiction

Day 1: Craft Share	Day 2: Craft Share	Day 3: Craft Share	Day 4: Craft Share	Day 5: Progress Share
Day 6: Progress Share	Day 7: Process Share (How do you research your topic?)	Day 8: Content Share	Day 9: Content Share	Day 10: Content Share
Day 11: Small-Group Share (Content Share)	Day 12: Process Share (What types of problems have you run into in your small groups? How have you solved them?)	Day 13: Small-Group Share (Content Share)	Day 14: Small-Group Share (Content Share)	Day 15: Small-Group Share (Choice)
Day 16: Small-Group Share (Choice)	Day 17: Small-Group Share (Choice)	Day 18: Process Share: (How are the small groups helping you grow as writers?)	Day 19: Process Share (How are the small groups helping you grow as writers?)	Day 20: Progress Share (What did you learn in this unit of study that you could continue using in future units?)

Notes

This unit of study began with immersion (days 1–4); Ellen used craft shares to expand on this work. She then used days 5 and 6 to celebrate particular students' breakthroughs and help other students set new goals. On day 7, she conducted a process share because she had observed that the kids did not have many ways of gathering research for their topics. On days 8–10 she conducted whole-class content shares as a way to prepare students to do similar work in their small groups. On day 11 the students worked in small groups; on day 12 they processed how the small-group work went. On days 13 and 14, the kids, in small groups, discussed the content of one another's writing. On days 15–17 the small groups chose the types of conversations they would have. On days 18 and 19, Ellen conducted process shares during which the kids reflected on what they were learning in their small groups. Finally, on day 20, Ellen conducted a progress share during which everyone reflected on current progress and made new goals for the next unit of study.

Bibliography

Atwell, Nancie. 1998. *In the Middle: New Understandings About Writing, Reading, and Learning*. Portsmouth, NH: Heinemann.

Anderson, Carl. 2000. *How's It Going?* Portsmouth, NH: Heinemann.

Avery, Carol. 2002. *. . . And with a Light Touch: Learning About Reading, Writing, and Teaching First Graders*. 2d ed. Portsmouth, NH: Heinemann.

Brinkloe, Julie. 1985. *Fireflies*. New York: Simon & Schuster.

Calkins, Lucy. 1994. *The Art of Teaching Writing*. Portsmouth, NH: Heinemann.

———. 2003. *The Nuts and Bolts of Teaching Writing*. Portsmouth, NH: Heinemann.

Calkins, Lucy, and Mermelstein, Leah. 2003. *Launching the Writing Workshop*. Portsmouth, NH: Heinemann.

Clay, Marie. 1998. *By Different Paths to Common Outcomes*. Portland, ME: Stenhouse.

Crews, Donald. 1992. *Shortcut*. Hong Kong, China: South China Printing Company.

Dewey, John. 1938. *Experience and Education*. New York: Collier.

Elbow, Peter. 1993. "The War Between Reading and Writing—and How to End It." *Rhetoric Review* 12(1) (Fall): 5–24.

Fletcher, Ralph. 1993. *What a Writer Needs*. Portsmouth, NH: Heinemann.

Fletcher, Ralph, and JoAnn Portalupi. 2001. *The Writing Workshop: The Essential Guide*. Portsmouth NH: Heinemann.

Gibbons, Gail. 1999. *Pigs, Pigs, Pigs*. New York: Holiday House.

Gibbons, Pauline. 1993. *Learning to Learn in a Second Language*. Portsmouth, NH: Heinemann.

Graves, Donald. 1983. *Writing: Teachers and Children at Work*. Portsmouth, NH: Heinemann.

———. 1994. *A Fresh Look at Writing*. Portsmouth, NH: Heinemann.

Hansen, Jane. 1987. *When Writers Read*. Portsmouth, NH: Heinemann.

Heard, Georgia. 2002. *The Revision Toolbox: Teaching Techniques That Work*. Portsmouth, NH: Heinemann.

Henkin, Roxanne. 1998. *Who's Invited to Share: Using Literacy to Teach for Equity and Social Justice*. Portsmouth, NH: Heinemann.

Hindley, Joanne. 1996. *In the Company of Children*. York, ME: Stenhouse.

Katz, L., and S. C. Chard. 1989. *Engaging Children's Minds: The Project Approach*. Norwood, NJ: Ablex.

Keats, Ezra Jack. 1962. *The Snowy Day*. New York: Penguin Books.

Keene, Ellen, and Susan Zimmermann. 1997. *Mosaic of Thought: Teaching Comprehension in a Reader's Workshop*. Portsmouth, NH: Heinemann.

Mercer, N. 1994. "Neo-Vygotskian Theory and Classroom Education." In *Language, Literacy and Learning in Educational Practice*, ed. B. Stierer and J. Maybin. Clevedon, UK: Multilingual Matters.

Moffett, James, and Betty Wagner. 1983. *Student-Centered Language Arts and Reading, K–12: A Handbook for Teachers*. 3d ed. Boston: Houghton-Mifflin.

Morrison, Toni. 1998. "The Site of Memory". In *Inventing the Truth: The Art and Craft of Memoir*, ed. William Zinsser. New York: Houghton Mifflin.

Newkirk, Thomas. 1989. *More Than Stories: The Range of Children's Writing*. Portsmouth, NH: Heinemann.

Rhodes, Lynn K., and Curt Dudley-Marling. 1996. *Readers and Writers with a Difference: A Holistic Approach to Teaching Struggling Readers and Writers*. 2d ed. Portsmouth, NH: Heinemann.

Short, Kathy, and Carolyn Burke. 1991. *Creating Curriculum: Teachers and Students as a Community of Learners*. Portsmouth, NH: Heinemann.

Willems, Mo. 2004. *The Pigeon Finds a Hot Dog!* New York: Hyperion Books.

Wood Ray, Katie. 1999. *Wondrous Words: Writers and Writing in the Elementary Classroom*. Urbana, IL: National Council of Teachers of English.

———. 2001. *The Writing Workshop: Working Through the Hard Parts (and They're All Hard Parts)*. Urbana, IL: National Council of Teachers of English.

Index